Bandages & Benevolence
by John Weeks

I owe my life, for which I am truly grateful, to the skills and care of the surgeons and nursing staff in the Kent and Sussex Hospital in 1939 where I spent 3 months following operations for bilateral mastoids due to complications of Measles and Whooping Cough.

I owe my career to the nursing staff who inspired me to become a Nurse.

Following general training and midwifery I returned to the Kent and Sussex Hospital as a night sister and ward sister that was a formative period of my career. I returned some years later as Chief Nursing Officer to the Tunbridge Wells and Leybourne Hospital Management Committee that included Pembury, Kent and Sussex, Leybourne and East Grinstead hospitals and the 5 cottage hospitals and maternity Home.

It was very clear, throughout the professional and organisational changes that took place in the late 60's early 70's, that standards of care were constantly scrutinised and updated to keep pace with medical advances despite some of the very outdated accommodation in which care was delivered.

Several attempts to provide a new hospital were made both locally and nationally but eventually thanks to the hard work of many people, the new Tunbridge Wells Hospital emerged, an example of a first class building fit for the purpose for delivering high quality of care.

This book is the result of a determined author to set out the history of the Health Care delivery to the Population of the Tunbridge Wells and District.

John Weeks has devoted many, many hours researching the archives and meeting a very wide range of people who recalled details and produced photographs. John, in setting out this history, has shown how the provision of health care has developed, despite the many obstacles that faced those with the responsibility for the provision of care.

A new hospital and a redesigned service provision between Maidstone and Tunbridge Wells will greatly assist in the provision of high quality care.

Audrey Emerton

Dear Reader,

It gives me great pleasure to introduce this book by John Weeks. When I read the history and perhaps even more when I looked at the photographs, I am not only fascinated by the developments that have taken place in our hospitals, but also to see the book as a piece of social history where the interweave of technology, values and social mores have combined in a mosaic which gives a far wider picture than simply the history of two buildings.

It also serves as a useful corrective to those who deny the notion of beneficial technical progress. When one looks at the equipment and the facilities available to health professionals now compared with that available in the 20's, 30's, 40's and 50's and the difference that new drugs have made to literally millions of patients worldwide is to recognise that for the vast majority of the population, life, as least as far as health is concerned, is better today.

It is also salutary to reflect as we look at the superb new hospital at Pembury and the improvements at Maidstone, that these too will look hopelessly out-of-date in 50 years time.

So to me the message that this book sends, by dint of diligent research and careful writing, is the understanding that we are only at one point on our journey and that constant and continuous improvement must continue to be our mantra for the future.

Anthony Jones
Chairman

Tunbridge Wells and its surrounding villages is one of the most beautiful parts of the country in which to live and work. But until recently its hospital facilities were among the worst in Britain.

It is almost unbelievable that in the 21st century, medical care was being provided in wooden huts and decaying mixed-sex wards. My predecessors – Sir Patrick Mayhew and Archie Norman – had all fought hard for a new hospital to be built and I was determined to continue this campaign. Local residents deserved better.

With the support of the local community, plans for a new hospital were developed but, as ever, funding was key. The only option available at that time was Private-Finance Initiative (PFI) funding and, in the end, the contract had to be signed in a matter of days, otherwise the funding was going to be lost. It was nail-biting stuff.

The old hospitals were full of memories and it is good to record their histories but I am proud that our community has moved forward with one of the best hospital buildings in the country.

Rt Hon Greg Clark, MP for Tunbridge Wells

Dear Reader,

This book provides a fascinating insight into how health services have changed both in the Tunbridge Wells area and nationally. We sometimes look back in nostalgia at what we perceive to be a 'better' time. This however ignores the huge improvements in people's health and our ability to treat conditions effectively.

Despite this, it is also striking how some of the issues remain constant throughout the period of the book. I read what must be one of the first complaints to the Tonbridge Union Infirmary which later became Pembury Hospital and was struck at the similarities to some of our complaints today (food and communications), this provides a valuable lesson to those of us responsible for providing healthcare that despite the technical advances we must not ignore the lessons of history.

Glenn Douglas
Chief Executive
Maidstone and Tunbridge Wells NHS Trust

From the Author

This book started with an investigation in a skip outside Pembury Hospital where some interesting slides were found and from then on an exciting and interesting story emerged. Now I'm not known for rummaging in skips but since I started this project I have developed a habit for rummaging in cupboards, skips, antique shops and just about anywhere bits of our story show up.

It was obvious that behind the decaying buildings of the Kent & Sussex and Pembury Hospitals lay an untold story. It wasn't long before the buildings gave up their story, cupboards and loft spaces all revealed hidden stores and documents and photographs and the architecture of bricked up doorways and the like. Of course the buildings don't make hospitals it's the staff, patients and volunteers who make the place and I have had the enormous pleasure to chat to so many of them who have spent time sharing their memories.

I would like to pay tribute to all those who have helped in telling their story because their story is our story too. I felt moved by the dedication and sheer hard work of those who worked here but also struck by the funny stories too.

What became obvious is the tremendous affection that our hospitals are held in throughout the community we serve.

In Tunbridge Wells we have a tremendous heritage we should all value and be proud of. We also have a new hospital to be proud of too, one of the most modern and up to date in the country. This book will put that new hospital in the context of our history and one day I hope someone will update this history – maybe even with another new hospital!

Lastly to keep our hospital running we have some of the best staff you will find anywhere in the National Health Service – working hard with dedication and humour. I have had the privilege to work with them at both the Kent & Sussex Hospital and Pembury Hospital before now working in the New Tunbridge Wells Hospital.

This is our story……

John Weeks

Contents

In the beginning...

The town of Tunbridge Wells is a relatively new one and owes its existence to the springs, discovered on the Common in 1606, that many people believed had health-giving properties. The reputation of the waters soon reached royalty, and royal visits started as early as 1630.

The town itself did not really grow until about 1700 – Tunbridge Wells remained part of other parishes until the 19th century. The ancient parish of Pembury can be traced back to the 12th century as a largely rural agricultural parish that has retained its village identity over the years, in contrast to Tunbridge Wells which has grown into a major town.

Our story begins in the early part of the 19th century with the Industrial Revolution making its mark across the country. In 1829, Britain had a population of about 24 million and infant mortality was high. Many died from infectious diseases such as smallpox and cholera, and often people died young – in fact, only 7% of the population was over 60.

The two communities were still small, with Pembury having a population of about 1,000 and Tunbridge Wells about 6,000. Tunbridge Wells soon became famous as a healthy place to live in and visit, with its reputation for clean air, sunshine and so-called medicinal waters gaining it popularity.

There was no National Health Service of course, but those that could afford it were able to employ the services of a doctor. Eminent doctors such as John Mayo lived around the town, and there was a good living to be made by those who set up in practice. There are stories of surgery being carried out on kitchen tables, but most poor people who got ill would take their chances with nature, using natural remedies found in the hedgerows handed down over the years.

It was against this backdrop that, in 1828 in the new town of Tunbridge Wells, a small dispensary was established in a property called 'Merry Vale' at the bottom of the High Street.

Its popularity grew, and in 1830 some 335 patients took advantage of the dispensary, with a further 445 being visited in their own homes. One of the objects of this charitable institution was to promote vaccination to try and control smallpox. The public were only too aware of the devastating effects of smallpox, and in 1830 over 554 patients were vaccinated by the three honorary physicians and four surgeons.

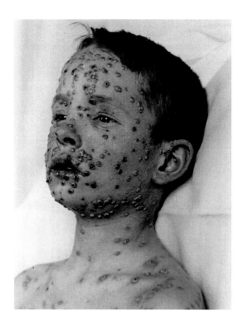

A child with smallpox.
Photo courtesy of Francine Paine
www.DartfordHospitalHistories.co.uk

Just as is the case today, the costs of running a hospital were significant. In its first year alone the accounts show the dispensary spent 13 shillings on bandages, along with £45 on drugs and 16 shillings on coal. Donations came thick and fast, including those from royalty, and with expenses of over £4,000 these were badly needed. The Duchess of Kent, Queen Victoria's mother, became a life governor of the dispensary in 1837.

In 1833, the committee of the Tunbridge Wells Dispensary first recognised the need for inpatient beds in Tunbridge Wells, and the first patients for surgery were admitted in 1834 - although there was no operating theatre and anaesthetics were still not in use. The increased demand saw building work start on a purpose-built infirmary in Grosvenor Road, which opened in 1842. A massive fund-raising campaign was well supported.

The poor and the unemployed, however, were often subject to the Poor Law, which required each parish to look after its poor in a parish workhouse. The saying 'on the parish' originated at this time, meaning one was receiving poor relief or reliant on the state. This system of dealing with the poor dated back to the first Poor Law Act of Elizabeth I, which dealt with the increasing burden of the poor following failed harvests and the fact that the monasteries, which traditionally dealt with the poor, had been dissolved by her father Henry VIII in the 1530s.

This system, however, was coming under increasing pressure, especially after the Napoleonic Wars (1793 – 1815). The price of corn meant high bread prices which, along with poor harvests, meant more people on the breadline. Civil unrest, riots and the horror of revolution in France in 1830 led to a change in government, which established a Commission of Enquiry into the Poor Law, which was close to collapse.

This was in an age when most agricultural workers were in tied cottages and lost their home when a job was lost. Poor nutrition meant susceptibility to disease, and the death of a main wage earner could spell disaster for a homeless and penniless family.

The government passed the Poor Law Amendment Act in 1834, which changed the system of Parish Poor Houses, or workhouses, and created unions with one central workhouse. This system was going to stay in one form or another until 1930.

The Board of Guardians, who were responsible for administering the Poor Law locally, met in the Tonbridge Parish Workhouse on 7th November 1835, representing ten of the surrounding parishes who were to be merged into one union. They accepted an offer to buy land at Sand Hill, Pembury, for £1,000 and appointed local builder Mr Calder to build the new workhouse at a cost of £4,152, with labour being supplied from the parish workhouses. The building was originally designed for 400 inmates.

The Tonbridge Union Workhouse, as it was to be called, began to take shape on this quiet country road on a hill, changing it for ever.

There the story of the two institutions begins – Pembury, a Poor Law institution managing on as little as possible, and Tunbridge Wells, a modern infirmary supported by the great and the good, seeking the very best skills and equipment that were available.

Chapter 1

Please sir can I have some more...?

The newly appointed Board of Guardians held their first meeting on the 8th of October 1836 at the new union workhouse - an event which was to continue unbroken until April 1930, when the Public Assistance Committee of Kent County Council took over. The workhouse was completed in September 1836, taking the first inmates in November.

The workhouse system of Victorian England has become synonymous with dark, prison like buildings, poor food and suffering and punishment regarded with horror by today's standards. From another point of view some argue that it was a first attempt at the welfare state, with the government taking responsibility for the poor. For many, the first introduction to workhouse life is Charles Dickens tale 'Oliver Twist' written about 1837 in which the child is harshly treated and dares to ask for more food at mealtimes before being admonished by the thundering Mr Bumble.

In 1866 Charles Dickens wrote to Dr Joseph Rogers, a Medical Officer at the Strand Workhouse:

"Few anomalies...are so horrible...that the poor should creep into corners to die rather fester and rot in such infamous places".

But was the Tonbridge Union Workhouse as bad as this national reputation?

It was certainly based on the National System, with a design pioneered by Sir Francis Head, the Assistant Poor Law Commissioner for Kent, with the house divided up so that men and women were separated, as were children. Its foreboding appearance on the hill, with its dark bricks and small windows circled by an iron fence and high brick wall, would have made it a place to be feared. However, there is some light with many examples of compassion by the Guardians amongst harsh punishments and conditions. Later, the Tonbridge Union Workhouse would host some of the most enlightened Guardians and reformers of their time.

The Staff of the workhouse were appointed by the Board of Guardians and approved by the Poor Law Commissioners in London, later the Local Government Board. The Guardians were appointed by election from local ratepayers, although many people were excluded from the vote in the early days as it was restricted to land owning ratepayers and excluded women, who were also at first prevented from being Guardians.

Many of the Guardians were local farmers, magistrates and gentry, each one representing one or more of the parishes that made up the union. The costs of the workhouse were met from the Poor Rates, and as ratepayers they had a vested interest in keeping costs as low as possible.

The workhouse was in the day, to day, charge of the Governor (later called the Master) who was both appointed by and responsible to the Board. George Gittens was appointed as the first Governor but he died forcing the Board to appoint Thomas Hadley on a temporary basis until Sgt John Harrison of the Grenadier Guards was appointed in August 1837, along with his wife who became the first Matron. One of the first instructions the Guardians ordered was to raise the walls around the Workhouse to prevent escapes.

In the same year another Governor was needed when Harrison was charged with misconduct and drunkenness and resigned forcing them to advertise for another Governor. Sgt William Blyth and his wife were appointed in September 1837.

Most workhouse Masters were ex Non Commissioned Officers from HM Forces, as they were deemed to have the necessary qualities to keep the house and the inmates in good order.

The Poor Law Board took over from the Poor Law Commissioners, with a Cabinet Member in charge for the first time, in 1847, following possibly the biggest scandal of the Poor Law era. Guardians reported appalling conditions at the Andover Workhouse, exposing the horror of girls being sexually abused, inmates forced to eat pig swill and suck the marrow from bones to survive, punishments included sleeping in the mortuary with bodies at night.
The country was truly appalled, and the Poor Law Board came under increasing scrutiny from both Parliament and the public. There is no evidence that such a harsh regime ever existed at Pembury, but the exposure of such conditions at Andover certainly changed the public's attitude to the system, and there was more interest in what went on over the wall and in the welfare of the poor generally. The local newspapers covered the Board meetings in increasing detail.

Infectious diseases

The first crisis to deal with was an epidemic of smallpox which spread rapidly through the building in the harsh winter of 1837 into 1838, forcing the Board to build an isolation ward at a cost of £600 so the sick could be isolated from the healthy. The isolation hospital was a wooden structure and not replaced until the new isolation ward was constructed in 1892. This later became Mary Ward. In July 1838 there were six deaths from smallpox three of which were children. The first winters of the new workhouse were very hard and the winter of 1837 saw daytime temperatures of -11C at Greenwich with deep snow.

In 1840 the Government passed the Public Vaccination Act, which required the Medical Attendant appointed by the Board of Guardians to vaccinate against smallpox. It was not just smallpox that caused death and disfiguring illness – diseases such as measles, scarlet fever and cholera were all prevalent often killing the old and the young. More epidemics followed in 1847, with 32 cases of measles and scarlet fever. During the next 50 years the Board of Guardians at Pembury aggressively used their powers to force children across the area to be vaccinated against smallpox, and any parent who failed to comply was brought before the Magistrates.

In England in 1848 over 62,000 died from a cholera epidemic, and there were to be two more before the century was out. It would not be until John Snow's theory of waterborne transmission of cholera that the disease could be tackled effectively. The various Public Health Acts of the latter nineteenth century, led to improved sanitary conditions, and curbed the spread of disease.
Typhoid which was also waterborne, and typhus, spread by lice were also commonplace even at Pembury.

Concern was expressed at the state of the water supply in 1848 when the Master proved it was unfit to drink by passing a lantern down the well which would not burn due to the 'badness of the air'. Arrangements were made for alternative clean supplies. However concerns about the drains and the bad smells continued for several years after, until water from the town main was connected to the workhouse.

Tuberculosis, often referred to as the white plague, was also rampant. In the nineteenth century it was responsible for 33% of all deaths in England. Poor nutrition and overcrowded housing were all factors in its spread. Scarlet fever was also widespread, killing over 34,000 in England in 1863, with 95% of all cases in children under 10 years old. The opening of isolation fever hospitals by local councils such as the ones at Hawkenbury, Capel and Tonbridge, enabled infectious patients to be isolated from crowded environments.

TONBRIDGE UNION.
NURSES.

WANTED, for the Hospital at the Tonbridge Union, a MAN and his WIFE, to fill the offices of NURSES in the male and female wards, at a salary of £40 per -annum and the usual rations.

Applications and testimonials to be sent to the Clerk on or before the 3rd March next. The appointment will take place on the 11th March, but no candidate need attend unless written to for the purpose.

No travelling expenses will be allowed.
By order of the Board,
W. H. WALL, Clerk.
Tunbridge Wells, 12th February, 1859.

The original hospital building
Courtesy of Adrian Line

The sick, infirm and insane

The Guardians did their utmost to keep the able bodied poor out of the workhouse by granting 'out relief' in the parishes where relieving officers appointed by the Board would administer cash or food benefits, especially flour, to those in need in the parishes.

Where exceptional situations arose, such as periods of high unemployment, they would pay the wages of the poor to work on local projects, including road building or farming local landowners' fields.

The workhouse, of course, soon began to be dominated by the sick, aged and infirm, and a dedicated hospital building was built in 1856 (pictured above), which was later used as a children's ward, nurses' home and then offices. This building meant, for the first time, the sick could be separated from the rest of the house. However it soon became overcrowded.

The staff who looked after the sick were not trained in the early days, and were nearly always inmates themselves, and received benefits in kind such as extra rations.

The Master recorded that in 1844 the Medical Officer ordered that the 'men nurses' were given two glasses of gin a day. These men nurses were inmates of the workhouse.

Often the insane were also admitted into the workhouse. The definition of insane was, however, broad and at first, included those with learning disabilities and epilepsy to name a few. Terms such as imbecile and idiot were commonly used in the registers. Later Commissioners in Lunacy frequently inspected those in the care of the workhouse and moves were made to admit all those regarded as lunatics to the Asylum at Barming near Maidstone but this cost the Guardians money. Many of the insane suffered serious injuries in suicide attempts and accidents, several with severe burns from incidents involving clothing catching fire.

In 1854, the institution occupancy was 84 men, 98 women, 72 boys and 72 girls in the workhouse with the infirmary block housing 22 male beds, 23 female beds and ten maternity beds.

The beds were in demand in winter of 1867 when smallpox again rampaged through the workhouse, along with measles. Even Mrs Revenell the infirmary nurse contracted smallpox.

Education
The children were required to be educated by law, and at first the dining hall was utilised as a school room but later a school was built as part of the 1856 hospital wing development. In 1871 there were 60 boys and 100 girls in the workhouse. 50 of these were infants and attended classes in the workhouse.

One of the first schoolmasters in February 1837 was dismissed for using 'unduly harsh punishments' on a schoolboy.

The advert for the next schoolmaster and mistress appeared in 1838, requiring 'a man and wife without family. Must be Church of England and be used to the National School System of Education.' A joint salary was offered of £50 per year including a room and rations.

Discipline was expected of the schoolmaster and he was carefully watched by the Master. During 1860 the schoolmaster was dismissed for meeting his daughter in the road outside and taking her to the pub in Pembury. He then came back later and entered through a window after lights out. An account of another disciplinary encounter appears at the end of the chapter.

Older children attended the village schools, as was common in most rural workhouses. There are stories of the children being taunted as they were taken to school in Pembury, even reports of cabbages being thrown at them as they were taken through the village. The school had two brick paved yards one for girls and one for boys. In 1877 50 children were attending classes in the building and a further 25 attending industrial training, including needlework. Many children ended up as apprentices or in domestic service, but some were enlisted in the Coastguard or Navy. There were some more interesting apprenticeships such as a cricket ball maker! Others were allowed to emigrate to Canada or America by sea, with a small amount of money from the Guardians to start a new life abroad.

Religion and The Chapel

The Church of England played a big part in Victorian life including the workhouse where the chaplain would be instrumental in everything from education to discipline. The Sunday service was held in the dining room but following representation from the Rev Saint of Groombridge Place the Guardians agreed to build a chapel. They laid down strict conditions on its use including that it would remain under their control. They also specified that a partition should be not less than six feet high to separate the sexes.

The total cost was £650, and although separate entrances for men and women were built when it was constructed in 1863, there is no evidence that the partition inside was ever built. It was built in the Gothic style, with a tiled floor and remains largely unaltered to this day including its Victorian blackboards carrying The Ten Commandments and other religious instructions for teaching the inmates.

It was originally built with plain glass windows with the exception of the main stained glass window of the Good Shepherd and other typical scenes such as the distribution of bread to the poor. Other stained glass was added later, including several to commemorate hospital staff

Some of the inmates of other faiths were allowed to attend their own acts of worship in Tunbridge Wells, including several Catholics, but were always accompanied by one of the workhouse staff.

The chapel was listed by English Heritage in 2007 and remains a key feature of the Pembury site. Now that the rest of the buildings have been demolished it stands proud as the last remaining link between the workhouse and the best that the twenty-first century NHS can provide.

The Chapel - Exterior and Interior
© The Tunbridge Wells Project

Births and deaths

The Civil Registration of Births, Deaths and Marriages started in 1837 and the union system was the administrative area for each registration district.
Birth and Death registers for the Tonbridge Union are still in existence and show that the first baby born at the new union house was Francis Neale in November 1836.

The register starts in December 1835 at the previous parish workhouse in Tonbridge and moved to the Pembury building on completion. Deaths remained fairly constant until the late Victorian period with between 24 and 33 deaths a year of which about five were children under five years old. Nearly all the births recorded were illegitimate.

By 1896, there was an average of 70 deaths per year, mainly as a result of the increased population being seen in the new infirmary, but still a similar infant death rate was recorded.

The causes of deaths in addition to old age were diarrhoea, gangrene, typhoid, diphtheria and TB. The deceased were sent back to the parish they came from in coffins made for and stored at the workhouse. If they were vagrants or came from the local area they were given a paupers burial paid for by the parish, and ended their days in an unmarked grave in the local churchyard or burial ground of the parish they came from.

For many years there were rumours that paupers were buried at the hospital, but this is not true – the Victorians were great ones for record keeping and records were kept of each and every death in the workhouse and where they were buried.

Tonbridge Union Workhouse showing farming land
© *Peter Higginbotham www.workhouses.org.uk*

The treatment of the dead was something Guardian Amelia Scott was interested in, and in her recollections she talks about the way the dead were managed.

"One day in the year 1901, while passing through the archway that connected the male and female wards, I met a procession coming from the female wards. It was made up of four decrepit old workhouse men who, in their stained oyster coloured corduroy suits, were wheeling a truck similar to the ones on railways stations – a platform with screeching small iron wheels. The truck was used to bring linen from the sick wards but instead of dirty linen it bore a shell-like coffin, with a loose lid and, within, a daughter of the King of Kings. The coffin was jolted so severely that the lid fell off to the ground. Nothing could break the repose of her who slept her last sleep, but for me the comfortable creed "Alls right with the world" was profoundly shaken."

Her investigation of the mortuary drew more words: *"The only mortuary was a shed in which one would have hesitated to place a bicycle. It had an earth floor like a potting shed. At the dark end the dead were in rows on shelves reaching to the roof like a ghastly bookcase."*

Amelia Scott established an appeal and within a year a new mortuary, post-mortem room and chapel of rest had been built at Pembury.

Vagrants

One of the biggest challenges was accommodation for casuals or vagrants. In 1872 a new reception block was added which contained the work cells and the Labour Master's office. After the institution stopped taking casual vagrants in the 1930s this block was transformed into Outpatients, Pathology and later Blood Transfusion.

Vagrants would be given a bed for the night and food, but were required to work before being released. The new block contained work cells to facilitate this process. These small cells had bars on the windows, and inmates were forced to break flint stones until they fitted through the bars in the cell. The Guardians reported that the amount of stone to be broken was 4 cwt, a lot less than some other workhouses, whilst women were expected to do 10 hours of washing or scrubbing.

The vagrant population would swell significantly during the Kentish hop picking season. The accommodation at this time was so tight that marquees had to be erected on the gardens to cope with the demand.

The vagrants quarters and Labour Master's House
Inset: Hammocks used by vagrants (pictured in London)

15

Amelia Scott also had something to say about the treatment of vagrants.

"I recall the utter dreariness of the long wards in use both day and night. Stakes of iron about a foot high were driven into the ground in two rows about six feet apart. At night hammocks would hang there with brown blankets. There were no chairs or benches and by day men sat on the floor. The food was served on wooden trays without plates or knives or forks. It consisted of bread and cheese. There were tin pails of skilly, a kind of porridge. Large white mugs were dipped into the pail. It can be imagined what happened when epidemics were rife. There were two stoves, one at each end for use in winter only."

The Cell blocks at Pembury

One of the Hospital Wings added in the 'Pavilion Style' advocated by Florence Nightingale.

Discipline and good order

Discipline and order were key to the workhouse regime, and those who chose not to follow the rules were disciplined. Punishments were entered in the Master's Journal where details of crimes and punishments were recorded. In 1854 the Master recorded that 'the able bodied got out on Sunday evening and broke 340 panes of glass.' The ring leaders were rounded up and five were sentenced to two months and five to six weeks hard labour at Maidstone Gaol.

He recorded that John Botting was sent to Maidstone Gaol for 14 days for refusing to work, and Hannah Joy sent to work cells for two hours for insubordination. Physical punishment was often used and in 1861, Henry Catt was given 18 lashes with a birch rod by the schoolmaster for throwing a knife at meal time.

The conduct of the inmates was carefully watched and Louisa Heath and Sarah Marshall were sentenced to 14 days in the Maidstone House of Correction for riotous conduct and in 1861 John Richardson was locked up for two hours for being in the wash house with the washerwoman. Other punishments included being given rations of dry bread and water for two days for using bad language and straitjackets were used to restrain those who did not co-operate.

Discipline also applied to the staff, and a nurse fell foul of the Master in 1858 when she was dismissed for both admitting the poor to the workhouse without permission and being absent for one hour. Later, another nurse was dismissed having been caught at three o'clock in the morning outside the infirmary picking peas. A pauper working in the kitchens was also reprimanded for selling bones and fat for 2d.

Many escaped, however, from the restrictive conditions of the workhouse to take their chances with clothing and food they had stolen. Each case was recorded carefully and the local constabulary informed. Rewards were sometimes offered to catch those who absconded, and the Master was sworn in as a special constable with powers of arrest.

Jubilee celebrations 1910
© *Peter Higginbotham www.workhouses.org.uk*

Work

In common with other workhouses inmates, mainly women were put to work picking oakum, which is described below. This was tough work and involved picking apart old ropes into fibres, which were usually moulded with tar and stuck by years at sea with salt. The fibres then sold to HM Chatham Dockyard for use in the Navy to repair ships.

In 1853 Thomas Bennett was sentenced to 14 days' hard labour at Maidstone Gaol for refusing to pick oakum. The saying 'money for old rope' comes from the picking of oakum. This account is contemporary with oakum being picked at Pembury:

"... prisoners were given a weighed quantity of old rope cut into lengths equal to that of a hoop stick. Some of the pieces are white and sodden looking ... others are hard and black with tar upon them. The prisoner takes up a length of junk and untwists it, and when he has separated it into so many corkscrew strands, he further unrolls them by sliding them backwards and forwards on his knee with the palm of his hand until the meshes are loosened. The strand is further unravelled by placing it in the bends of a hook fastened to the knees and sawing it smartly to and fro which soon removes the tar and grates the fibres apart. In this condition, all that remains to be done is loosen the hemp by pulling it out like cotton wool, when the process is completed ... The place is full of dust... the shoulders of the men are covered with brown dust almost as thick as the shirtfront of a snuff taker ... the hard rope cuts and blisters their fingers."

Criminal Prisons in London and Scenes of Prison Life, first published in 1862, H. Mayhew and J. Binny.

In addition, men were tasked with chopping wood, breaking stone for repairing roads and numerous farming tasks around the site. As with any public institution there was pressure to keep costs down and in 1850 the Board decided to buy an additional twelve acres to use for farming. The sale of pigs and produce kept the costs down and helped to provide food for the inmates.

Female oakum pickers
© Peter Higginbotham   www.workhouses.org.uk

The Sandhill Infirmary

The workhouse developed into two distinct sections – the infirmary for the sick and the paupers' workhouse. This was an important development as Dr Joseph Rogers estimated in 1875 that only 8% of workhouse inmates nationally were fit. The infirmary block which was later used by Maternity Wards was completed in late 1890.

The large building programme started in 1885 on the Pembury site required the Board to borrow £15,000 at 3.5% interest over 30 years. The start was a Guardian's Committee report into overcrowding in the small infirmary wing and consultation with the Local Government Board. This went on for nearly two years before plans were approved and building commenced.

The result was four new blocks – three to house the sick and one to house the infirm and elderly. More nurses were employed including Assistant Nurses on a salary of £25 a year, who were paid an extra 2/6 for looking after infectious cases. The adverts were careful to point out that they had to be single women without children.

Even after this no provision had been made for an operating theatre. In her recollections of times at the Union, *'The Passing of a Great Dread'* Amelia Scott wrote

"I recall in those early days noticing the anteroom of a certain ward was in disorder and no convalescing patient occupying it. On enquiring I learned from a patient that it was being prepared for an operation. Yes, the very table that was used for daily meals was to be used as an operating table! Carefully scrubbed, I admit but there it was and there was no getting away from the fact."

The wards in the original hospital block at Pembury
© Peter Higginbotham www.workhouses.org.uk

During 1900 a Superintendent Nurse was employed and people no longer had to be destitute to benefit from the infirmary at the workhouse. However, the stigma of going to the workhouse still remained.

The care of the sick in the infirmary was basic and the nurses had little or no training until the Poor Law Institutions (Nursing) Order 1914 came into force, requiring all nurses to be trained. It also made orders to improve hygiene, including making an order that no more than one inmate could be bathed in the same water.

The original entrance archway in 1962

The workhouse buildings – the water tower and pumping gear was taken out in the 1980s

The Local Government Board, who had taken over from the Poor Law Board, introduced easier conditions for the elderly in 1899, when they encouraged unions to allow couples to stay together and have additional rations such as extra tea.

In 1893, the entrance lodge was completed along with a new mortuary, drying and ironing rooms added to the main house.

So, what were conditions like in the Victorian Infirmary at Pembury?

The British Medical Association conducted a survey of hospitals in the 1890s and visited Pembury in 1894. Their report gives an impression of the facilities.

The report starts by painting a picture of an idyllic surrounding on a hill with *"a view a millionaire might envy in some of the loveliest scenery in Kent."*

It describes the old hospital built in 1856, containing 80 beds used exclusively for male infirm patients. It mentions each room holding eight to ten beds heated by fireplaces and lit by gas lamps:

"The new infirmary built in 1890 – 1893 gives expression to the modern opinion of the requirements of a hospital for the sick – even if they happen to be paupers. The wards are oblong having windows on either side with bedsteads placed between them. Two fireplaces in the ward – smooth coloured painted wall surface, coloured matting down the middle and pictures give it a cheerful appearance.

Each bed has an allowance of four blankets on a straw and hair mattress."

They criticised the operation of maternity however and the fact that as there was no children's ward: *"It cannot be desirable to keep children apart in health and then allow them to mix with the sort of loose women who frequent the maternity department of a workhouse."*

On the male side they found 60 beds on two floors and they noted that the nursing load was heavier on the male side.

The isolation hospital had 33 beds and they praised its design of being able to lock off and isolate cases as required.

They were concerned that medical and surgical cases were treated together - on the same ward.

They considered staffing and found that there were no trained nurses by day and only one at night, and the untrained nurses on duty depended on pauper help in all of the wards.

They also examined the menu and were *"struck by the monotony of the meat diet, which is always mutton."*

Louisa Twining (1820 - 1912)

Miss Twining was a member of the wealthy Twinings Tea family and became a leading philanthropist. A friend of Florence Nightingale, she was influenced by visiting a London workhouse and seeing the conditions. She was in regular correspondence with Government Ministers and Civil Servants. It was difficult to get into workhouses and visit those inside and after getting nowhere with the Poor Law Commission she got the issues raised in Parliament. If she could not persuade Parliament then she could persuade 63 highly respectable residents and formed the Workhouse Visiting Association in 1857. Louisa then became a full time workhouse reform campaigner bombarding the Press and Government with campaigns and letters and visiting workhouses all over the country much to the upset and alarm of Guardians. In establishing the Workhouse Nursing Association in 1879 she set about improving the quality of nursing care available in workhouses up and down the country. After becoming one of the first female Guardians once they were allowed to stand for election in the 1880s in London she continued to campaign to improve standards. After retiring to both Worthing and Rochester she settled in Tunbridge Wells and was appointed to the Board of Guardians in 1893. In the next few years she set about introducing reforms including continued boarding out of children, visiting and comforts for the elderly. She was instrumental in the completion of the infirmary blocks, and one of the wards was named after her.

Amelia Scott (1860 - 1952)

Miss Scott was elected to the Board of Guardians and continued Louisa Twining's reforming work. Amelia was a huge campaigner for women's issues becoming Vice President of the National Union of Women's Suffragette Societies and a committee member for The National Council for the Unmarried Mother as well as National Council for Women.

She gave many speeches on the welfare of children and trained as a social worker in Rotherhithe. At the workhouse she paid a great interest in gaining girls employment with large houses and expanding remote boarding houses for children. Her work continued after the Guardians were abolished serving on the House Committee at the Hospital and as a visitor. She was also decorated by the King of Belgium for her tireless work to support Belgian Refugees in Tunbridge Wells during World War I. Amelia campaigned and obtained a new mortuary, chapel of rest, operating theatre and wards at Pembury. Her efforts were not just directed at Pembury, her interest in women and in particular mothers led to her leading a fund raising campaign to open a maternity home in Tunbridge Wells as a tribute to the sacrifices made during the First World War. It opened in Upper Grosvenor Road before moving to Calverley Park Gardens. She campaigned for Women Police Constables in Tunbridge Wells and after her work in the First World War received the most votes of anyone standing for election in the 1928 Guardians election. After her support for the development of the new wards, one of the new surgical wards was named after her in 1937. Amelia Scott Ward continued until its change to the Children's Unit in 2007.

Disciplinary Case against the schoolmaster

Letter to the Board of Guardians from the Master:

"I am sorry to intrude on your valuable time but I cannot suffer the refractory conduct of the schoolmaster to pass unnoticed. On Saturday morning I locked the passage door agreeable to your answer of my last report. The schoolmaster demanded a key and I refused. At which he damned me and swore at me. He blackguarded me and called me a d—d scoundrel, d—d villain, insolent rascal and if it were not for the law he would pull my nose. He states that myself and Matron should not enter the school which he will sort out. The boys and girls are getting more and more disorderly. Two girls Sarah Bromley and Gemma Powell aged 14 charges the schoolmaster with improper conversation to them whilst they were making the boys beds. He entered the room laughingly shut the door and told them he would show them how to turn down beds down that was the way: the way to lay young maids down so: flat on the beds. I can find no untruth in this report so therefore stated it for the information of the Board.

Yours obediently"

A small committee including the chaplain were tasked to investigate determining that:

- The schoolmaster was guilty of insubordination

- The order for closing the passage was inconvenient

- No instance of neglect of duty has been proved

- No charge of indecent conduct with girls is proved.

The schoolmaster was reprimanded but he resigned in protest and left the same day.

Part of the Amelia Scott Window

The Ten Commandments

The window depicting the Good Shepherd in the chapel
All pictures © The Tunbridge Wells Project

Workhouse dormitory buildings
Courtesy of Adrian Line

TONBRIDGE UNION.

CONTRACT FOR

FLOUR.

The Board of Guardians of the Tonbridge Union will be prepared at their Meeting on Friday, the 16th of December, instant, at Eleven o'clock, at the Union Workhouse, Sandhill, to receive Tenders for the supply of Flour.

Good Second Flour,

(Agreeable to the Sample to be seen at the Workhouse.)

(To be delivered at the Workhouse by the Sack and at the Relieving Stations by the Gallon.)

Tenders may be made for the whole, or any one, or two, of the undermentioned Districts, or for the Workhouse.

1st. District.	2nd. District.	3rd. District.
ASHURST.	CAPEL.	BRENCHLEY.
BIDBOROUGH.	HADLOW.	HORSMONDEN.
SPELDHURST.	TUDELY.	PEMBURY.
Part of TUNBRIDGE.	Part of TUNBRIDGE.	

All Tenders must be filled up in printed Forms, to be obtained on application to MR. RUSSELL, the Governor of the Union House, and no other form of Tender will be received. They are to be sealed and marked " *Tender for Flour,*" and are to be sent to or delivered at the Office of the Clerk, No. 4, Belvedere Terrace, Tunbridge Wells, at the expense of the Contractors, on or before the 14th of December inst.

The Contract is to commence from the 25th of December inst., and to continue until the 25th of March next; and the Flour contracted for, is to be delivered at the Contractor's expense. The payments will be made monthly. As often as any Flour furnished shall be disapproved by the Board other Flour, good and satisfactory, must be furnished in lieu thereof, or the Board shall be at liberty to furnish other Flour, and the difference in price must be paid by the Contractor.

The Contractor is to sign an Agreement and be prepared with the names of Sureties for the due performance thereof. The names of the Sureties to be stated on the day above mentioned.

The Guardians reserve to themselves the right of rejecting the lowest or any other tender.

W. H. WALL, *Clerk to the Union.*

Tunbridge Wells, December 3rd, 1859.

WILLIAM BRACKETT, PRINTER, UPPER PARADE, TUNBRIDGE WELLS.

Chapter 2

The Tunbridge Wells Dispensary and Infirmary

Expanding healthcare

In the growing town of Tunbridge Wells, with its now widespread reputation for health, sun, fresh air and the spa waters, the small Infirmary with its dispensary, which had moved to Grosvenor Road in 1842, was rapidly improving and expanding, taking over several adjoining houses and extending its facilities.

It was described as one of the finest buildings in Tunbridge Wells, set back from the road, with large windows in the ward area and a large outpatient hall below.

The Tunbridge Wells Infirmary c.1840

The hospital always tried to keep in touch with advances in healthcare and frequently launched appeals to improve and update. A major advance occurred during 1848, when subscribers raised enough money to build a purpose-built, dedicated operating theatre – the first in Tunbridge Wells. This replaced the room in outpatients which was converted twice a week for the purpose. This was only a year or so after the introduction of anaesthetics into England.

Mr Isaac Hargraves, one of the original committee members and generous benefactors who helped to found the hospital, died in 1856 and a marble bust was commissioned to commemorate this man's dedication to healthcare in Tunbridge Wells. The bust stood in the entrance hall of the Kent & Sussex Hospital until its closure, and was moved into the Education Centre of the new Tunbridge Wells Hospital when it opened. His modern vision of the very best healthcare provision for Tunbridge Wells has been carried on through the years.

Lord Abergavenny, whose seat was Eridge Castle, became the first patron, and the Marquess of Camden of Bayham Abbey Estate, the first President. The relationship between the two families and the hospital movement in Tunbridge Wells continued right through the 20th Century.

Isaac Hargraves (1790 - 1856)

A son of a surgeon from Brighton he first came to Tunbridge Wells as assistant to Mr Prince a surgeon in Tunbridge Wells in 1812 aged 22. He then trained at Guy's Hospital before starting in Tunbridge Wells in 1817. He set up his practice at Buckingham House on Mount Ephraim. He was instrumental in setting up the Tunbridge Wells Dispensary even paying for the Operating Theatre. He cared for those who were less fortunate and those who could not afford the full amount would often find accounts settled by him and he frequently sent food and medicines to those in need with strict instructions that the source should not be divulged.

He became the Senior Surgeon at the Tunbridge Wells Hospital and Chair of the local branch of the British Medical Association. He died in 1856 and is buried at Rusthall Church.

A stone tablet was unveiled at the Kent & Sussex Hospital to commemorate this association when hospitals were handed over to the NHS in 1948. The inscription reads that it marks:

"the association of their families with the hospital from its beginning and to remember 120 years of devoted service by the men and women of this place."

It was removed from the hospital and placed in the new Tunbridge Wells Hospital when it opened.

Throughout the middle of the nineteenth century the numbers of patients seen increased still further. Some 2247 outpatients were treated and 123 inpatients in 1850. Medical staff treated fifty cases of smallpox in their own homes to prevent admission to the infirmary. The infirmary rules prevented admission of infectious cases and in 1864 the locals presented a petition asking for fever wards to accommodate the sick, but the committee rejected the idea in favour of house visits. Later the council would open its own fever hospital at Hawkenbury, which later became Hawkenbury Hospital and would be joined by others at Dislingbury near Pembury and Capel, near Paddock Wood.

The Matron, Mrs Cox earned £32 and 10 shillings a year but was not a trained nurse and retired in 1857. The job of Matron was given to Mrs Odam, a capable austere lady, who kept a tight reign on expenditure but again was not a trained nurse. This was the era when Florence Nightingale had returned from the Crimean War and set up the first nurse training school, which would set the standard for the future.

In 1865, the committee ended mixed-sex wards and provided separate wards for male and female patients. The committee also approved the supply of brandy and wine to outpatients on the orders of the Medical Officer, at a cost of £30 per year, and by 1870. The cost had risen to £66 per year. Alcohol was seen as an essential stimulant and good at restoring health in the Victorian era.

After overcrowding in parts of the infirmary, plans were drawn up to expand and rebuild parts of the site, and by 1870 new wings were opened, giving much better accommodation costing over £4000, again raised from public subscription. Pelton's Illustrated Guide to Tunbridge Wells published in 1883 described the Infirmary as:

"a handsome building of sandstone with every arrangement for their comfort and convenience."

Patients could only be admitted or treated with a letter of recommendation from a member of the committee or a subscriber, and in 1871 instructions were issued to ensure the circumstances of all those who applied were checked to see if they could afford to pay for their care. Those who subscribed one guinea a year or a donation of ten guineas became governors, and were entitled to nominate one inpatient and two outpatients to be on the books at any time. Yearly subscribers of eleven shillings were entitled to have one patient on the books at any time. The hospital, however, frequently treated those who were poor and disadvantaged even without a letter.

In Tunbridge Wells, home visits to those lucky enough to either be recommended or afford it averaged 56 a day during 1873. Interestingly, the average stay for an inpatient in 1873 was 51 days. This had reduced to 28 days by 1914.

Homeopathy
During the second half of the nineteenth century there was a flourishing homeopathic medicine interest in Tunbridge Wells, which started with the Tunbridge Wells Homeopathic Dispensary in 1854, the Tunbridge Wells Parade Homeopathic Dispensary in 1860, the Tunbridge Wells and West Kent Homeopathic Public dispensary in 1863 and the Tonbridge and Southborough United Homeopathic Dispensary in 1855. They amalgamated under the Tunbridge Wells Homeopathic Hospital in 1902.

This building, still in use in Church Road, had inpatient beds and an operating theatre and was expanded in the 1920s with additional ward space. A homeopathic practice would continue until 2007.

Further down into the town Dr George Abbott founded the Tunbridge Wells Ear and Eye Hospital which opened in 1878 on the Pantiles but was enlarged in 1896 and moved to Mount Sion in 1900, this hospital operated along the same lines as the General Hospital. Dr George Abbott a renowned Eye Surgeon, who also founded the Technical Institute, saw the hospital expand its specialist services to capacity providing a full range of surgery.

Tunbridge Wells Eye and Ear Hospital

He provided lectures and classes in the hospital basement in all manner of adult education subjects to locals. He was a renowned Geologist and founder member of the Tunbridge Wells Natural History Society, which set up the first Tunbridge Wells Museum.

Suicide
In 1873, a special meeting of the Board was called to discuss actions of the House Surgeon, Mr Rix who refused admission to a patient who had attempted suicide. The Board approved his decision, considering that such persons must be either criminals or lunatics or both. This decision continued in force until 1891 when it was rescinded provided an attendant was present for the patient. The nearest asylum for those who were mentally ill, was at Barming, near Maidstone.

Increasing demand

The increasing population and better treatments led to expansion once again, and, in 1865, an assistant house surgeon was employed for the six busiest months of the year, along with funds being raised to enlarge the infirmary by purchasing adjoining houses at a cost of £1,700. The infirmary employed its first surgeon dentist in 1865. The increase in work, however, meant a change in the rules, approved in 1877 which discontinued the visiting of patients in their own homes.

The harsh Victorian winters were a major risk to the ill and poor, and the Board found much difficulty in keeping the wards warm in the winter with coal fires. Following a gift from Lady Molyneux, a hot water pipe heating system was installed in the infirmary, with much better results.

At a special Board meeting in 1884, the Governors agreed that the infirmary should be renamed the General Hospital at Tunbridge Wells. The main need was that the term infirmary was often taken to mean the infirmary attached to the workhouse and the stigma attached to it was reflected in the attitude to the Tunbridge Wells Infirmary. Later it was renamed The Tunbridge Wells and Counties General Hospital, reflecting the service to rural parishes surrounding Tunbridge Wells.

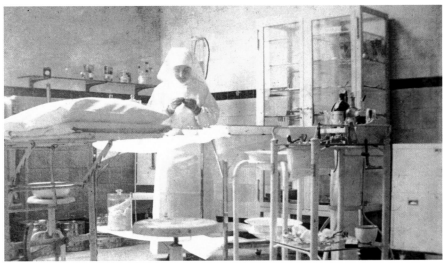

Operating Theatres at the General Hospital in 1918

The first purpose-built children's ward was opened following a donation by Mr Jones Gibb of £2,000 during 1885.

A note in the finance archives tells us in 1885 the whole of the General Hospital was insured for £5,500. This was to prove useful when, in 1886, a fire broke out in the dispensary, although the damage was limited.

The work of the hospital became renowned and in 1887, the year of Queen Victoria's Golden Jubilee, over 45 people applied for the post of house surgeon to work in Tunbridge Wells.

Nursing

The Matron, Mrs Odam, retired in 1890 after 33 years service and was voted an honorarium of 100 guineas, and a sum of £230 invested for her to provide her with a pension of £40 per year in recognition of her good work. Over 98 applications were received for the post of Matron. This marked a change in nursing at the General Hospital. Until this time most nurses were untrained and fulfilled menial tasks such as scrubbing floors. A correspondent of the era said many night nurses were:

"old women addicted to alcoholic liquors who frequently drank the stimulants (alcohol) prescribed for patients".

Staff of the General Hospital

The new Matron, Miss Forbes, was a trained nurse having trained in the Florence Nightingale School at St Thomas' Hospital in London and became the first trained nurse to hold the position of Matron in Tunbridge Wells. On appointment, the nursing establishment was changed to four trained nurses, five probationers and one nurse's maid. All of them lived in at the hospital. The Matron's log book however shows that some recruits were not up to Matron's exacting standards:

Constance, employed in 1894 – described as:

"useless nurse, found to be careless, lazy, and dirty and not kind to patients"

Mabel, employed in 1896 – described as:

"unfit to be a nurse in every way, she is hysterical, careless and shirks any duty she considers unpleasant."

Catherine, employed 1900 – described as:

"having been found unsatisfactory in work and conduct, was granted a further three months trial after this was dismissed as there was no improvement in her work."

Matron Forbes retired in 1900 and Mrs Lessey, another nurse trained at St Thomas' Hospital, arrived to run the hospital. Most trained nurses employed were from St Thomas' hospital, as the nearest training school.

Most people would, however, be nursed at home and so-called Home Nursing Courses especially those run by the Red Cross and St John Ambulance were very popular. The Kent Nursing Association and the District Nursing Institution provided access to nurses able to help in the home. These organisations were given a boost in 1897 when Queen Victoria made District Nursing one of her Diamond Jubilee causes, raising money for the provision of nurses later forming the Queen's Nursing Institute.

Expansion

The hospital was closed in 1890 for three weeks in December due to an outbreak of scarlet fever which originated in the children's ward. This unpleasant and highly infectious condition was common in Victorian times. Isolation was strictly enforced during outbreaks and patients transferred to the Isolation Hospital.

Additional land was purchased in 1894 at a cost of £2,900 raised by voluntary contributions to expand the hospital further, and in 1895 a fire water main was provided into the hospital from the new public water supply. The end of 1896 saw an increase in beds to 55, treating over 500 patients a year with outpatients seeing some 4300 patients a year.

During 1897, the year of the Queen's Diamond Jubilee, a total of £3,000 was raised by the public to build a children's hospital, which was built next to the General Hospital. This was part of a bigger programme of works which saw the increase in beds, accommodation for staff, theatre and outpatients department. The foundation stone was laid in 1903 and completed with a fund of almost £1,400 in 1904. A shelter on the roof, donated by Mr R Pelton, named the 'The Pelton Shelter', was constructed close to the Children's Ward to offer open air treatment for children with TB and other diseases to maximise fresh air and exposure to sunlight.

The General Hospital. The Post Office now stands on this corner

The fundraising campaigns frequently featured 'Leo', a huge St Bernard Dog belonging to the Matron of The Tunbridge Wells Nursing Home who had a collecting box and went through the town and door to door collecting money, as did the local fire brigade which had a dog too, called Jack.

" A mile of pennies" – a fund raising initiative that aimed to lay a mile of pennies around the hospital

In 1906, the Annual Meeting of the National Council for Women met in Tunbridge Wells and were shown around the hospital, and described the children's ward as the:

"prettiest ward for babies and children we have ever seen, its walls are tiled to the ceiling, pale yellow in colour and panelled with charming illustrations of fairy tales - colouring is exquisite."

Leo - the fund raising St Bernard

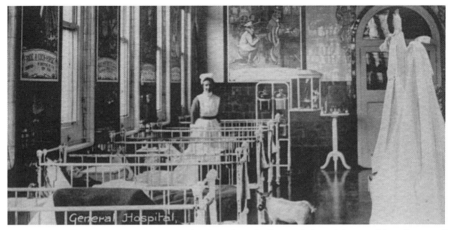

*Despite attempts to move the tiles when the hospital closed they could not be saved
and were demolished with the building*

X-ray

X-ray a new science was brought to the hospital in 1897 by local benefactor
Sir David Salomons, who also later in 1910 purchased a Finsen Light for the
treatment of Lupus (skin TB), a disfiguring but common disease of the
Victorian Era. It meant that the General Hospital in Tunbridge Wells was one of
the first outside London to have an X-ray Department.

He became friends with X-ray pioneer George Howard who had lived in
Tunbridge Wells and was one of the first to show the benefits of X-rays.
He was honorary radiographer to the General Hospital for 20 years working
with Sir David who financed a lot of his experiments and ideas.

Sir David exchanged the plant in 1910 as a result of improvements in
technology and purchased all the radium needed for Tunbridge Wells meaning
the hospital had an extraordinary reputation outside London. He was keen that
the radium could be used by doctors in the local area as a way of bringing
much needed income into the hospital.

Dr Barnardo's opened a home in Park Road Tunbridge Wells in 1902 for sick,
orphaned and convalescing children, employing a number of nurses and
working closely with the Tunbridge Wells Hospitals.

Dr John Barry 1815 - 1881
Dr Barry was Physician to the General
Hospital and the first Doctor with a specialist
interest in disease of the heart.

He wrote essays on endocarditis and travelled
widely as well as being very popular in
Tunbridge Wells. He died in Tunbridge Wells
and is buried in Rusthall.
Courtesy Royal College of Physicians London

The opening of the New X-ray Room ©courtesy of Salomon's Museum,
Canterbury Christ Church University

Chapter 3

The Edwardian Era and the Great War

The new century

At the start of the 20th century a raft of welfare legislation was passed to improve the conditions of the poor and needy, some of which came out of the Royal Commission on the Poor Law. The School Meals Act 1906 and the School Medical Service 1907 aimed to improve the health of school children. The Old Age Pensions Act 1908 and the National Insurance Act 1911 all aimed to provide for those who needed help as a result of old age, injury or unemployment.

Some free medical care was provided for those insured through a panel doctor system, and those with TB were entitled to some free treatment. The class system, alive and well in Edwardian Britain, ensured that panel patients did not stop private patients obtaining their care. There are stories of panel patients having to queue at the back door at inconvenient times whereas private patients arrived at the front door to be greeted by a maid and offered tea in the drawing room at a time to suit them.

There were draw-backs however – you had to have been in work to make contributions and it did not apply to women at first. Nationally, there was a decline in infant mortality and the death rate in the population, especially from infectious diseases came down. In Tunbridge Wells, rates were already below the national average. In 1904, the national infant mortality rate was 159 per thousand who would die before one month but in Tunbridge Wells it was 88.5 per thousand. The population of the workhouse started to decline as legislation improved the conditions of the poor.

Pembury

The workhouse had developed into two distinct sections, the hospital and the workhouse. The Sandhill Infirmary, as the hospital was later called took on a distinct identity with the appointment of Elizabeth Robb as Superintendent Nurse in 1904. Her salary was £55 per year with accommodation and rations provided. She trained at the Mile End Infirmary in Whitechapel and had known Louisa Twining.

For the next twenty years she set about changing the infirmary into a modern hospital. Miss Robb was a strict, almost austere, woman but a very capable organiser, able to get the most from her staff and the limited resources available. Her position was a lonely one as she reported to the Master and Matron who were keen to keep costs down. A Poor Law Journal reported at the time:

"The Superintendent nurse is cautioned that in all matters pertaining to the treatment of patients she is under the control of the Medical Officer; She is in all other matters bound to recognise as her superior the Master of the Workhouse. The position of Superintendent Nurse is therefore one that requires much tact otherwise there may be and often is a good deal of friction between administration and medical heads of establishment."

All of the linen, equipment and drugs were paid for by the workhouse and the goodwill of the Master and Guardians was crucial in running the hospital.

Naming of the wards at Pembury

The Wards at Pembury had all been named by 1900. The first to be named was the Louisa Twining Ward, which was later changed by Guy's Hospital in 1939 to Queen Ward and never changed back. This meant that the memory of Louisa Twining passed into Pembury history without note. Havelock Ward was next, named after Sir Henry Havelock (1795 -1857). A popular hero in Victorian Britain, he was a Major General in the Army and died fighting in India.

The neighbouring ward was Gordon Ward, after General Charles Gordon (1833 – 1885), another national hero, who was made Governor of the Sudan following his distinguished service in the Crimean Wars. A friend of Florence Nightingale, he died in the Khartoum Siege in 1885 after mapping the River Nile.

On the Male side Clarence Ward, which was originally named after the Duke of Clarence was renamed Bright Ward, by Guy's after the physician Richard Bright pioneer of renal diseases and Brabazon Ward after the charity renamed by Guy's in 1939 to Addison Ward, after Thomas Addison, the physician who discovered Addison's Disease. Cheverton Ward was named after the Chair of the Guardians, Mr George Cheverton, a local homeopathic chemist and pharmacist who also ran a dispensary near the General Hospital.

The coronation of HM King George V and Queen Mary in 1910 provided the opportunity for a parade and fair at the workhouse with games and a firework display. Commemorative medals were struck and given to those taking part, along with a fine dinner.

The nursing staff consisted of Miss Robb, two charge nurses and eleven probationer nurses. Miss Robb reported that adverts were not well responded to but in 1915 she appointed two probationers at a yearly salary of £28 with board and lodgings paid for by the Guardians. At the time nurses lived in attic rooms and small rooms upstairs in the old hospital building in very cramped conditions.

The continued development of Poor Law nursing was highlighted in the British Journal of Nursing in 1912, when a campaign was launched to get nurses trained and working in Poor Law Institutions the same status as those working in voluntary hospitals such as the General Hospital.

Amelia Scott wrote, *"All honour to the nursing staff under the Poor Law – often undervalued by their own profession, losing rank when they left the voluntary hospitals where they trained – yet undertaking far more intricate nursing - namely the chronic sick with cancer, TB and other diseases without a resident Medical Officer."*

The work of the main workhouse went on, with Amelia Scott one of the main forces for change. Her friend, later Clementine Churchill, wife of the wartime Prime Minister, was also co-opted as a Guardian for a short time.

In the height of the Second World War in 1941 she wrote to Amelia, from 10 Downing Street saying:

"I am afraid I was not of very great use, being so inexperienced - but I do feel I learned something there ....."

Tunbridge Wells
The Friendly Societies

The General Hospital continued to expand and so did its need for funds. The main fundraising events were Hospital Sunday where the whole town would come out to watch a parade of the organisations in the town with the aim of raising money for the hospitals. The fundraising day made a significant contribution to the hospital along with Pound Days where a table was laid out for donations of produce and church collections.

There was a close relationship with the so-called friendly societies, of which there were many in Tunbridge Wells. These societies collected money each week from members and were able to obtain letters to allow treatment of their members in the hospital as well as other benefits. Some of the largest societies included The Foresters and the Tunbridge Wells Equitable Society. Funds left over were often donated to the hospital, and the societies enjoyed a close relationship until the NHS started.

A vision

A driving force in securing further funds was Joseph John Webb, often referred to as 'JJ', who took up office as Assistant Secretary and Dispenser at the Hospital in 1905. He spent the rest of his life raising interest in developing hospital services in Tunbridge Wells. He persuaded people that a new hospital was the only answer to the overcrowding at the General. He was instrumental in acquiring the land for the new Kent & Sussex Hospital but sadly died before he could see it built. His funeral, attended by the Marquis of Camden, brought Tunbridge Wells to a standstill as the town paid tribute to this visionary man.

The Dispensary sold aspirin for the first time to the public in October 1905.

In 1910, the nurses of the Tunbridge Wells Hospitals sent flowers and condolences to the widowed Queen Alexandra on the death of King Edward VII. Queen Alexandra wrote a card, thanking the nurses for their warm wishes. 1910 was also the year that the architect of nursing, Florence Nightingale, died. Amelia Scott had made reference to her obituary in the Nursing Mirror:

"It is not often given to a reformer to live till the accomplishment of a great purpose has been brought about. This grace was hers who has passed from us full of years and honour. Once before the world has rung with her praises, when, after her return from the Crimea, the nation strove to express its gratitude. She chose then to turn the national sense of thankfulness to good account in training women to spread the light, and it is true now as ever that those who follow in her steps are her best memorial. Her insight was never clouded. She looked to the next generation to carry on and perfect what had been begun ... And she leaves us with a wonderful heritage of hope for the future ... her memory will never fade while there are disciples to follow her lead against ignorance, dirt, and disease ..."

A message sent to nurses at the General Hospital from HM Queen Alexandra

The rules of the General Hospital stated that inpatients could only be admitted on Tuesday mornings unless it was an emergency. Patients could not be admitted without a change of linen and security to defray the cost of removal or burial. Emergencies were seen by the House Surgeon at 9 o'clock each morning.

Dr Tucker, interviewed in 1950, recalled his time at the hospital in 1911 using Chloroform Anaesthetics. There were two Resident Medical Officers on duty and the rest of the staff were honorary visiting consultants. There was no lift at the time and patients were carried up and down stairs to theatre. He remembered that patients brought in their own eggs, jam and soap.

First World War

At the outbreak of war in the summer of 1914 Parliament authorised the call up of half a million troops. Some of these camped out on the common in Tunbridge Wells prior to deployment to France. The General Hospital provided care to those ill or in need of care, however soon casualties came back to Britain in huge numbers and hospitals would be required to do their bit. A decision was made to offer 60 beds for military casualties and although this meant a reduced capacity for local people it was widely supported.

Voluntary Aid Detachments, principally managed by the Red Cross and St John Ambulance soon took on the task of setting up auxiliary hospitals in homes either given or requisitioned for the war effort. At Tunbridge Wells, houses at Kingswood and Broomlands were turned into hospitals. The VAD hospitals in Kent treated over 114,000 patients by the end of the war and nationally VAD hospitals treated over half of the total number of wounded brought back to the UK from the continent.

The first batch of war casualties arrived in a fleet of private cars on September 27th 1914 from Chatham Docks, and by the end of the war in 1918 the hospital had treated over 1,700 soldiers from HM Forces, some with terrible battle injuries, including amputations.

The hospital was asked to help treat wounded Belgian soldiers from the front who arrived in 1915. The management board decided to convert the Outpatients Hall into a ward for these soldiers. HM King George V sent the hospital pheasants and hares from the Sandringham Estate to help the hospital feed those who were wounded, and the Marquis of Camden sent over 5,000 cigarettes to the troops on the wards.

Leading the nursing care of patients throughout the war was Matron Ada Smith, who trained at the Charing Cross Hospital in London, becoming a senior sister there before moving to Tunbridge Wells and taking up the position of Matron at the General Hospital in 1903. Her work in Tunbridge Wells was rewarded when she was presented with the Royal Red Cross in Silver by HM King George V, at Buckingham Palace, after the war, recognising her work in leading the nurses not only at the hospital but providing leadership and co-ordination around the local wartime VAD hospitals.

In March 1918 a new X-ray unit was commissioned at the hospital by Sir David Salomons as a memorial to his only son, a victim of the HMS Hythe Disaster. This disaster touched the lives of many people in West Kent, over 155 soldiers died with 43 dead from Tunbridge Wells alone, when the troop ship HMS Hythe was hit by another ship and sank off the coast of Gallipoli in 1915. Sir David had founded the regiment at the start of the war and never forgot the troops who had died.

Sir David was a former Mayor and trustee of the hospital for many years, having installed the first X-ray apparatus in 1897. This department gave service to many war pensioners across West Kent in the years after war.

Between 1897 and 1918, over 57,000 X-rays were taken and a thriving electrical treatment room had developed. The electrical treatments included hot and cold baths and massages with electrical currents. These were often applied to malformed limbs and curvature of the spine.

The last soldier left the hospital on February 8th 1919. The end of the war, however, saw the hospital in financial difficulties for the first time. It became in debt to the bank by £4,230 in 1919, which had increased to £6,300 by the end of 1921, which equates to nearly a million pounds by 2010 values. The high cost of food and materials after the war hit the hospital hard and appeals were being made every week for more donations. A newspaper appeal reflected the stark choices, revealing they needed five times the current income to survive. A discussion about all patients having to pay was held and generated a much needed flood of donations, but the financial crisis saw the resignation of Sir David Salomons in 1920.

The hospital was carrying out more than a thousand operations a year, with over 20,000 electrical treatments alone by 1921.

First World War toops outside the General Hospital in 1916

The Outpatient Hall converted in a ward for wounded troops. Matron Ada Smith is pictured in the centre

General Hospital Entrance 1920

The workhouse

The Local Government Board wrote to the Guardians at Pembury in January 1917, reminding them that: *"if the public cannot receive care at the General Hospital then they had a duty to make care available at Pembury".*

This perhaps was the start of a wider acceptance that care was provided to all in the hospital, and was not connected to the Victorian Workhouse of the previous century.

The need for accommodation for wounded troops and other war work meant the War Office commandeered many workhouses across the country. The Union at Pembury was keen to be part of the war effort and offered 250 beds for wounded soldiers transferred back to the UK from field hospitals in France. The military expressed an interest in this and plans were made to evacuate inmates from the workhouse to other poor law establishments across the South East. However, the military wrote to the Union in 1918 saying that they wished to acquire it for use as a driver training school, mainly for women ambulance drivers.

The Guardians, however, felt that this was not a good use of the beds offered in good faith for wounded troops. The Borough Council agreed and letters were hastily sent to the War Office urging them to reconsider the decision as the Guardians were ' by no means convinced of the necessity for the army to take over the institution…'. The appeal worked and as the armistice was signed the War Office wrote to the Guardians confirming that plans for the evacuation of inmates could stop. Amelia Scott spoke to the Courier who quoted her as 'being very disgruntled as it was not of sufficient national importance.'

The need for able bodied men to join the forces was acute and in January 1917, the war office wrote to the Guardians to remind them that if able bodied men of fighting age arrived at the workhouse the recruiting officer in Tunbridge Wells was to be informed at once by telephone.

In 1917, the infirmary was recognised as a minor training school by the General Nursing Council, and formal training began with nurses spending time at the General Hospital for surgical training, and at the East End Mother's Home in London for six months. However, to complete their training nurses had to go to other hospitals, especially Lambeth, where close ties were formed. Full training status was not given as the hospital still did not have a resident Medical Officer.

After the First World War there were many children without families and the government encouraged Guardians to recommend children for emigration to Canada , although at Pembury there was not the vast emigration that appeared in some other workhouses. Several children were sent including Annie Oliver in 1919 and Albert Oliver in 1920.

The Influenza Pandemic that swept through the United Kingdom after the war affected Pembury too. Beds were erected in every space possible. Maud Stibbon a nurse at Pembury interviewed in 1963 recalled wards:
"packed with patients, many died, on night duty I started to wash patients at 10 or 11 pm and it went on all night in order to get the work done before the day staff came on duty – it was so sad to see their faces – they were hard days."

There were serious food shortages towards the end of the war and throughout the influenza pandemic, and Guardians were advised that a 1lb bottle of Bovril was equivalent to two weeks supply of meat and to use this to avoid excess meat rations. Other shortages included salt and flour. The expansion of the farm at Pembury provided much needed extra rations of eggs, meat and vegetables.

In the October of 1918, the Courier reported the death of the Headmaster of St Augustine's School at the General Hospital from the 'scourge of the current epidemic of Spanish influenza.'

By the end of 1918, the War Office had dropped plans for the takeover of Pembury, and the hospital started a new era. It is not known if it was the local protests or the Armistice that stopped the plans, but Pembury would develop faster in the post war period than it had ever done before.

By the end of 1919 the movement to separate the workhouse from the hospital was gathering pace and in October it was officially known as the Sandhill Infirmary. Registrations of births and deaths began using the Sandhill address, removing some of the stigma of the having 'union workhouse' on the death or birth certificate. The first death registered at the new address was on 5th October 1919.

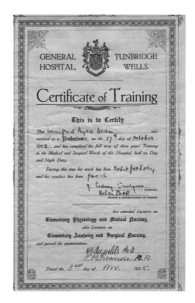

The Tunbridge Wells Maternity Home

In 1918, Amelia Scott led a campaign to build a Maternity Home and at a meeting proposed the resolution: *"The women of Tunbridge Wells are resolved to devote in thanks giving for peace to provide a Maternity Home".*

Over 1,400 people contributed and a home was opened in Upper Grosvenor Road which was officially opened by Mrs Chamberlain, wife of the Minister of Health in 1925. Later a new home would be opened in Calverley Park Gardens in 1930.

Two of Amelia Scott's main concerns were reducing infant mortality and the welfare of mothers. She was chair of the Infant Life Protection Committee for many years.

The 1970s saw more births take place in hospital, the home closed in 1978 and later became Highlands House, which provided accommodation for the two geriatric wards demolished to make way for the new Culverden Wing at the Kent & Sussex Hospital.

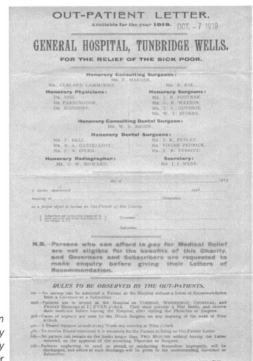

A Hospital Letter from 1919 – the only way to get in was by subscriber letter

Chapter 4

A new hospital for Tunbridge Wells 1920 - 1938

The 1920s started with unemployment and economic difficulties, indeed a general strike would be called in 1926. The country was getting back on its feet after the war years, and, despite significant financial problems the vision of a new hospital in Tunbridge Wells continued, while advances in social security and living conditions would soon see reforms to the Poor Law and the end of the workhouse.

The perfect site

It was as early as 1926 that discussions first took place to merge the General Hospital and Eye and Ear Hospital. The hospitals had long worked closely together and saw the benefits in providing care on one site, sharing the same support services. A search for suitable land for a new hospital took place and eight acres of land soon came on the market in Mount Ephraim. This site on high ground was deemed suitable and an appeal was launched to buy the land.

The land was the site of Great Culverden House, and the nurse's home, Burslem House, was constructed on the walled kitchen garden of the property. Previously, it was in the hands of Admiral Lucas, the first naval officer to gain the VC and who died in 1914. Upon the death of Mrs Lucas in 1924, the whole estate was offered for sale but did not realise the reserve figure so was sold off in lots.

The house and gardens were designed by Decimus Burton, who laid out Hyde Park in 1825.

The house was entered via iron gates and a brick archway from Mount Ephraim, roughly where the main entrance to the hospital was located.

At the end of 1927, the appeal fund stood at £37,676. The fundraising campaign has become legendary.

Great Culverden House

The Peanut Club

The Courier newspaper launched the Peanut Club. The club, which had its own children's fun magazine edited by *'Aunt Agatha'*, appeared each week in the Courier. The real Aunt Agatha was Mrs Gordon Clemetson, a member of Courier staff who became a cult figure amongst children locally – she started as an office girl and eventually became Editor in Chief of the Courier Group.

The scheme started by accident when she offered a bag of peanuts to anyone who could collect a shilling's worth of Queen Victoria Bun pennies, as part of a fundraising idea that reporters were challenged to come up with. These old pennies carried an old portrait of Queen Victoria with her hair in a bun and were quite rare. Then, eventually, one child produced a bag and the Peanut Club was born! The club, which expanded fast, raised money from fairs, fetes, fun days and collections - plus the shilling donation to join.

All proceeds went to the building fund. The club, by 1934, had over 20,000 members and by the time the Tunbridge Wells Scheme ended in 1948 it was the biggest single contributor to the building fund. Members of the club came from all walks of life, and the whole ship's company of HMS Revenge became members after a girl enrolled her uncle, a crew member, who then got the whole ship's company to join.

The toys for the playroom were collected by sailors from the ship, who came to Tunbridge Wells in June 1934 whilst in dock at Portsmouth. The Courier reported the huge crowds who came to see them as they toured the hospital. The crew also sponsored a cot on the children's ward. The left-over food from their welcome dinner was passed to the hospital, where Matron had the joints made into cottage pies for the patients.

Celebrity members included Shirley Temple and the Archbishop of Canterbury.

Pets were also enrolled and given a special collar badge to wear along with a certificate. Aunt Agatha always replied to letters, and travelled many miles visiting club members.

The Motto and Pledge of the Peanut Club raising money for the hospital

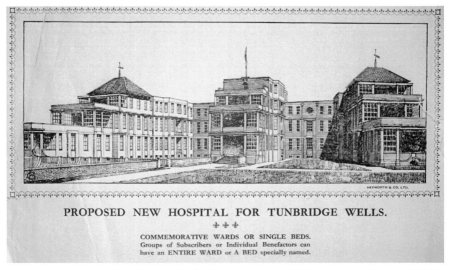

PROPOSED NEW HOSPITAL FOR TUNBRIDGE WELLS.

✛ ✛ ✛

COMMEMORATIVE WARDS OR SINGLE BEDS.
Groups of Subscribers or Individual Benefactors can
have an ENTIRE WARD or A BED specially named.

Part of campaign leaflet showing an artist's impression of the new building

A campaign leaflet was printed and local author A.A. Milne, creator of Winnie the Pooh and who lived at Hartfield, wrote an appeal for funds.

He said: *"We are, I'm afraid, asking you to give, not to get! No reason why you should, save for being that sort of person. But we do offer you a sporting chance, the chance that just by your gift a life may be saved; and this certainty, that giving is the only form of spending which can never bring regret."*

The money needed was increasing however, and vigorous fundraising was needed if the hospital was going to be built at all.

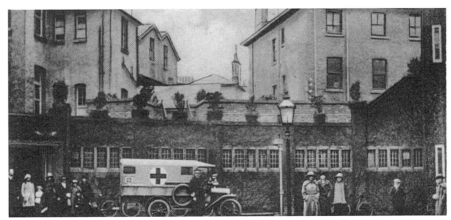

Casualty Entrance. General Hospital C.1920

Pembury

The hospital at Pembury was being modernised where possible, and one of the most important developments was its approval as a nurse training school in 1924. The arrangement was that nurses would complete two years at Pembury then two years at Lambeth Infirmary. The General Nursing Council recognised this arrangement from March 1924.

The Nursing Act 1919 made provision for state registration of nurses and from 1923 the title State Registered Nurse came into use, along with set standards of education.

In October 1924, Miss Robb was succeeded as Superintendent Nurse by Miss Mary Harvey. One of the first problems she encountered was the disappearance of one of the student nurses . The police were called but she went missing for over three months with no explanation.

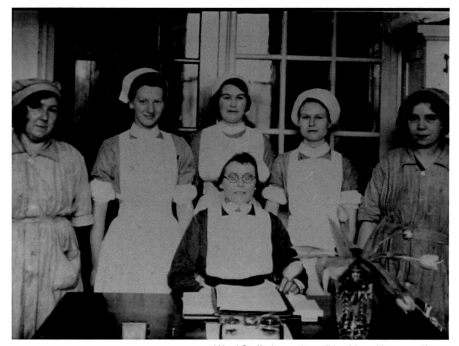

Ward Staff: domestics still in old workhouse uniforms

It was decided that meat for dinner would have to be carved by the nurses on the wards, but as Miss Harvey pointed out to the Master there were no carving knives – every item had to be approved by the Guardians.

She regularly pleaded for more staff, as at the end of 1924 there were only 15 probationer nurses, two trained nurses, three ward sisters and a sister tutor. She reminded the House Committee that the increase in treatments ordered by the doctors, and the increase in lectures for probationers under the new training scheme, were putting a huge burden on the nurses.

The hospital was struggling to maintain modern standards and Miss Harvey asked again in October for more pillows as: *"there is not even enough for one per bed"* In November she remarked in her report: *"a gas ring and small sterilizer is required for each block for the boiling of instruments. With the present arrangements, a saucepan on a coal fire, it is most difficult to teach the nurses to work aseptically."*

In 1926, the Operating Theatre was opened in the female block on the ground floor. However, ward nurses were required to scrub up to assist the surgeon as no dedicated theatre staff were employed until 1938.

It was lit by gaslight even though explosive anaesthetics were in use. Amelia Scott had campaigned long and hard for such a theatre and took pride of place at its opening.

Medical care was still provided by an outside Medical Officer, usually a GP from either Pembury or Tonbridge, appointed by the Guardians at a very basic salary. Dr Kirkness, a local GP from Pembury, was appointed Medical Officer of the infirmary from 1918 to 1926 and worked hard until his death to raise the profile of the work at Pembury.

In 1926, care was provided by various local GPs appointed as Senior Medical Officer by the Guardians, but a major step forward was the appointment of a full-time resident Medical Officer, the first being Dr Tom Davies, who later became a renowned Surgeon Captain in the Royal Navy. He was quickly followed by Dr Archibald Magill, who went on to become Medical Superintendent at Chatham Naval Hospital.

In 1928, a young doctor replied to an advert in the Lancet. He was to stay at Pembury for the next 40 years as a driving force for modernisation and change in developing a modern hospital service at Pembury. His name was Ernest Dudley Yarnold Grasby, and after a childhood in Devon he started his medical training at Guy's Hospital in 1921, qualifying in 1925.

His initial recollections of the first time he went through the gates sum up the hospital in that era: *"It looked very peaceful and inviting ... dotted with splendid trees. There were medical, surgical and maternity wards in the main building and, further along, isolation block and wards for the chronically sick. There was also a small operating theatre. I understood I would have my own personal maid. The paintwork was inevitably green and yellow - standard in every hospital I knew, Guy's and the naval hospitals too. They were immaculately clean and the nurses' uniforms were neat and tidy and clean too. I had a feeling that life was far from hectic at Pembury. I decided to apply for the post and started on 1st July 1928, initially for a 12-month appointment."*

After he started he had every Thursday afternoon off and the Senior Medical Officer paid a visit, although Dr Grasby pointed out: *"I suppose I saw him about six times in two years before he retired. I did call him once but I never called him again, and from then on I knew I was very much on my own."*

Mary Rowson, a nurse at Pembury in the 1920s, was interviewed in the 1980s and remembers there were no electric lights, just gas burners, no internal phones, and if a nurse was needed at night the other nurse would bang on a coal scuttle in the corridor until help arrived. She recalled that most work was done by pregnant or mentally deficient girls from the workhouse, under the direction of the nurses. She recalled: *"Could anyone imagine a more incongruous mixture than mental, epileptic children, TB patients and the Home Sister's bed sitting room all on one ward. Strangely enough though I enjoyed it!"*

In 1920, the hospital was inspected by the Ministry of Health. In her report, Mrs Andrews from the Ministry reported: *"heating arrangements appeared universally inadequate, markedly so in the children's hospital where the children had cold feet and hands, and on enquiry I learned that during the winter they are known to have chilblains.."*

At the time, children were nursed in a block near 'B' Block where radiotherapy would be based. The report ends with a commendation that the infirmary was well equipped and well kept.

Children were gradually being taken out of the workhouse system across the country, and the Poor Law Institution Order 1913 outlawed children over three years of age from being in a workhouse longer than six weeks. In 1920 the Ministry of Health wrote to Guardians across England saying there were still too many children in workhouses, and to speed up the process of boarding out or emigration.

The workhouse felt the effects of the miners' strike in 1920, when the Ministry wrote to the Guardians stating that due to the national emergency there must be no fires in bedrooms or corridors, and that lighting should be reduced: *"Where electricity is in use light bulbs must be taken out."* It ended by reminding Guardians of their duty to do their bit to conserve energy in the national interest.

One of Dr Grasby's duties was to present a report to the Board of Guardians. He said:

"Now that I had been there six months I was bold enough to suggest certain improvements which I believed would be helpful, and I also asked for a consultant surgeon to be available and for the services of an anaesthetist. The Board were sympathetic and a surgeon was appointed, and another Tonbridge man for anaesthetics when required. This was necessary as the number of acute surgical cases was increasing. I was told unofficially that changes would take place in the near future concerning administration and the future use of the infirmary. It was rumoured that Kent County Council would take it over and the number of wards would be increased."

The end of an era
In 1929, the Poor Law was abolished and the Poor Law Institutions were transferred to the Public Assistance Committee of Kent County Council. The Board of Guardians was changed to Guardians' Committees, which still had a strong say in the running of the institution. However, a central Public Assistance Committee ensured a more strategic overview of the provision in Kent.

The shortage of hospital beds led to an immediate building programme at the new Pembury County Hospital, as it was renamed by 1935. The Guardians however, did not disappear and were part of the new House Committee at the hospital. The press, who had reported every meeting, were excluded from all future meetings by order of the County Council – a move described as very undemocratic by the Tonbridge Free Press.

In order to make more room for the sick, most of the inmates were transferred to a new old people's home, run by Kent County Council in 1935, called Pembury Grange. Amelia Scott had long been an advocate of smaller homes for children and adults alike where those residents would not be institutionalised, calling for gardens and pastimes to keep people occupied.

Although seeking to leave after his marriage, the Board and, in particular, Amelia Scott persuaded Dr Grasby to stay. He was appointed Senior Medical Officer on a salary of £650 a year, and allowed to live out: *"I was consulted extensively on the modernisation of Pembury ... Even at that time it was clear Pembury was to become an important regional hospital, and it was even hinted that I could be appointed its Superintendent."*

Expansion

After the Public Assistance Committee took over the institution a programme of building commenced, to address the shortage of hospital accommodation. The new 'F' Block wards, named as Margaret, Elizabeth, Evelyn and Amelia Scott, were opened in 1933 costing £40,777, along with central heating costing £24,000, electric light in the theatre costing £100, a new pig sty and slaughter room costing £212, and a new nurses' home costing £15,010, named Woodlands House.

The total cost of improvements between 1931 and 1939 was £113,353 and saw Pembury enjoy the biggest investment in health facilities in Kent. The new wards were named after Princesses Elizabeth and Margaret, daughters of King George VI and Queen Elizabeth. Amelia Scott Ward was named after the long-standing guardian and pioneering social worker who had done so much for Pembury.

The theatre was carrying out between three and five operations a week, and the theatre register shows anaesthetics were usually given by Dr Grasby.

These included operations for osteomyelitis, a terrible infection of the bone hardly seen nowadays, excision of glands following TB, and - by the start of the war - many radical operations for cancer. The increase in surgery at Pembury meant an increase in costs too, as the cost per head increased from 27 shillings 10 pence in 1931 to 52 shillings in 1939.

The New Theatre at Pembury

In 1931, Mary Harvey left her post as Superintendent Nurse and was replaced by May Cussack until 1934. Her successor, Caroline Wheeler, had been appointed Assistant Superintendent Nurse in 1933 and had been Home Sister and Sister Tutor from 1930. She worked to develop the hospital until she left to move to be Matron of Hereford Hospital in 1940.

Dr Norman Jacoby, in his book 'A journey through Medicine', noted that when he arrived at Pembury from Guy's Hospital in 1939 the situation was very different to London: *"I discovered the real picture of TB (tuberculosis). The hospital had a small department for adults with pulmonary TB, and the state of their disease was such as I had previously thought as only historic, patients with huge cavitations, continuous coughing up of blood, grave anaemia and illness. It was quite extraordinary that so many of these people had not been thought of as really ill until it was terminal."*

By 1937, the hospital had 92 nurses, and a third medical officer was appointed at a salary of £250 per year. Children's facilities were improved in 1935 as well, with the opening of two new children's blocks, one as a nursery and the other as a hospital. The new wards were hailed as a real development, with each ward built in two identical halves to facilitate isolation on one side for infectious diseases. Balconies provided space for patients' beds to be wheeled out into the fresh air.

Its expansion was not met with universal approval and concern was expressed by the voluntary hospitals, including the Kent & Sussex Hospital. They were concerned that the free hospital service provided at Pembury might take away income needed to keep the new Kent & Sussex Hospital open. The Public Assistance Committee described facilities for the sick poor as insufficient and stated: 'It is the policy of the Public Assistance Committee to in no way impede the work of the voluntary hospitals.'

The introduction of resident medical staff and new accommodation enabled a full training school for nurses to be established on the Pembury Site in 1933.

Throughout the 1930s admissions to Pembury continued to rise:

	Admissions	Operations (MAJOR)	Operations (MINOR)	Road Traffic Accidents
1930	691	21	31	89
1932	869	32	44	89
1933	1268	114	103	169
1934	1573	151	112	192

In 1934, due to the rise in emergency admissions, a receiving ward was built costing £3,000 and the first X-ray facilities, costing £4,000, were opened soon afterwards. Before this, casualties were taken direct to the ward and those needing an X-ray went to the Tunbridge Wells General Hospital, for which the Institution paid a fixed subscription each year.

The huge rise in population in the area in the summer, due to the influx of hundreds of hop pickers, mainly from London, also caused an increase in patients to be seen. Many of these hop pickers lived in close contact with each other in huts, and infectious diseases spread quickly.

The hospital set about demolishing dividing walls built for the workhouse and changing brick courtyards to flower beds and lawns, to soften the site and try to change the atmosphere.

Staff of the institution in 1935

Master	1	Assistant Nurses	23
Matron	1	Children Attendants	1
Medical Officer	3	Relief Attendants	3
Chaplain	1	Cook	1
Clerks	4	Porters	2
Asst Matrons	2	Infirm Attendants	6
Supt Nurse	1	Domestics	17
Sister Tutor	1	Engineers/Gardeners	9
Charge Nurses	4	Male Nurse	1
Sisters	2	Staff Nurses	5

A new additional theatre was constructed in 1936 at a cost of £10,459. This was still used as a theatre even in the 1980s when the new main theatres closed for maintenance, but later became the Eye Day Care Unit in the 1990s.

Surgical operations increased significantly at Pembury from just 198 in 1932 to 238 in 1937. Admissions also rose from 691 in 1930 to 1572 in 1934.

So Pembury Hospital ended the 1930s almost transformed from its workhouse beginnings into a hospital that we would recognise today, except it had become a self contained community.

Dr Grasby commented: *"The site was completely self-contained – there were engineers, carpenters, painters, tailors, seamstresses, cooks, laundresses, orchards, a farm and a bakery."*

His son, Richard, recalled his visits and time spent there in the war as a child:

"The cobblers' shop was next door. Four elderly bootmakers sat in a row hammering away at the soles of heavy boots or cutting the shapes out of hides with deadly sharp pointed knives. I said "Good Morning" and they nodded. They could not speak because their mouths were full of little nails ... I rushed across the yard to the Bakery. I learned never to open the door while dough was rising. The bakers, Mr Owen and Mr Drew, white all over, white faces, hands and white trouser suits – every movement they made brought a cloud of flour.

Mr Woodrow was the Head Painter and a fine figure he cut, immaculately dressed and wearing a once-white coat with paint splashes of many colours. His team painted everything all the time, green and yellow indoors and green and white outdoors.

My favourite workshop was run by an expert cabinetmaker, Mr Weeks. He had a team of three carpenters and another cabinetmaker. His desk was nearest an open fire where a huge kettle and a glue pot hissed and bubbled all day. His tool box was five feet long with a great brass padlock on – bits and saws and tools of every type all lightly oiled and paced in their own baize-lined recess.

The boiler house, with its chimney some hundred feet high, stood behind a great mountain of coke – perfect for sliding down! The stokers who fed the flaming furnaces were tireless workers but, with their blackened faces, white rings round their eyes and peaked caps, were to us children terrifying. There were plumbers, too, who were in great demand due to the Victorian lead pipes.

Mr Turner ran the engineers' workshop and ruled it with an iron fist. A terrific team of gardeners worked on all spare soil, and the piggery was run by a wonderful character who did not acknowledge anyone and spoke to no one apart from his pigs. The waste food created a nutritious swill for the pigs.

Lastly Jack, the hospital horse – a well trained, useful horse. He pulled a farm cart and was experienced in ploughing and harrowing. The ploughman was a dignified tall upright man. He wore a white collar, narrow tie and black waistcoat with a gold watch chain."

Vagrants

There were big changes to the treatment of vagrants or casuals who used to call at the institution for their night's board and lodging.

The management of casuals was subject to meticulous regulations by the Ministry of Health, but on transfer to Kent County Council it was evident that these were not always followed. On arrival each vagrant was supposed to be searched, and anything on him was supposed to be removed before he was entitled to a bath and clean towel.

According to the report of the Public Assistance Committee: *"The habitual vagrant spent most of his time tramping the country and therefore had more hot baths than the vast majority of the population."*

Aged and infirm casuals were actively encouraged to give up their life of vagrancy and settle down in an institution. These old people's homes were opened by the County Council to care for these people, along with youth training centres for young people and children's homes for children, and so by 1930 there were only two child vagrants reported in the whole of Kent.

Kent & Sussex Hospital

On 6th June 1932, building work began on the new hospital. There was great interest in the building project – the biggest in Tunbridge Wells for many years.

The whole building employed 150 workers full-time for two years, greatly easing the local hardship in difficult economic times. The project used 1.75 million bricks and throughout the campaign the local community were urged to buy a brick or sponsor a bed or cot.

Construction of the Kent & Sussex Hospital

From the top of Ward 14 while under construction

Cecil Burns (1882 - 1969)

The hospital, designed by Cecil Burns, was built by
local builders John Jarvis Ltd.

Cecil Burns was born in Sutton and educated at Tonbridge School.
He trained under Sir Reginald Blomfield, beginning his practice in
Tunbridge Wells in 1906.

He served in the Royal Garrison Artillery in the First World War but was
gassed at the Battle of Paschendale in 1917 and returned
to Tunbridge Wells.

In the journal Khancrete Engineering published in the following year architect Cecil
Burns wrote an article about his design. He bestowed the cost saving design and
innovative use of reinforced concrete. The new idea of concealing pipes inside the
concrete walls was talked about, as well as the signature fire escapes on the end
of the wards. He discussed some of the small features such as the rainwater
ducts in concrete, with KSH stencilled in them.

He later designed the Kent & Canterbury Hospital.

Royal visit

Laying the foundation stone

The highlight of the building of the new hospital was the laying of the foundation stone by HRH the Duchess of York (later HM Queen Elizabeth the Queen Mother) on 19th July 1932. The day began with the arrival of the Duchess at the town border, where she was met by the Mayor and taken in an open-topped car to the hospital through streets lined with well wishers. The Duchess was very popular in the country and crowds flocked to see her – the Courier reported there were 'miles of smiles' along the route.

After inspecting the many voluntary groups, troops and veterans from the First World War she laid the foundation stone with a silver trowel, after placing a time capsule into the foundation stone which had current copies of The Times, Tunbridge Wells Advertiser, Kent & Sussex Courier, Annual Reports of the two hospitals and a copy of the programme of the day.

This time capsule was excavated in 2012 when the foundation stone was removed and transferred to the new Tunbridge Wells Hospital. The contents had not fared well with some entirely disintegrated by damp.

Troops line the route to the hospital

The Duchess then received fundraising purses from the villages and towns around the district before meeting the crowds, several of whom fainted and needed treatment by the St John Ambulance Brigade. The Duchess also named the Children's Ward the Princess Elizabeth Children's Ward after her daughter (later HM The Queen). This ward later became Ward 7.

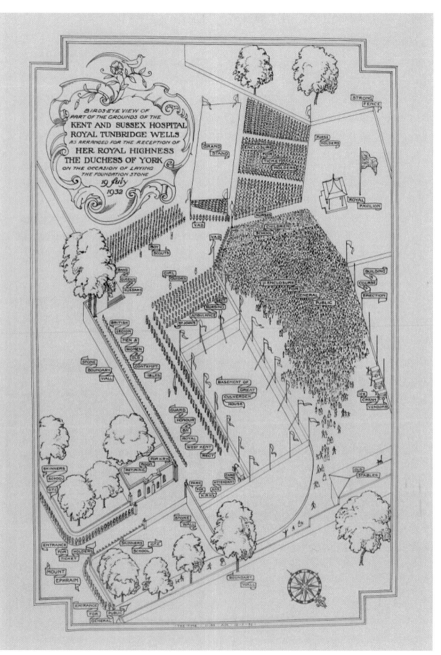

A plan of the Foundation Stone Ceremony by Cecil Burns

Laying of the Foundation Stone

Matron is received by the Duchess of York
Photo courtesy of Tunbridge Wells Museum and Art Gallery

Official opening

The building was finally opened on Wednesday 25th July 1934, amid bright sunshine, by the Marchioness of Camden with a special gold key cut for the occasion. In her speech she said: *"Those who are familiar with old hospitals must realise that they are sadly out of date and ill-equipped to meet the increased demand on the service. The new hospital, however, will provide ample accommodation and the best facilities for medical treatment under ideal conditions."*

The Opening Ceremony outside the children's ward

The hospital was still in debt to the tune of £14,000 at its opening. Appeals for it to open free from debt were printed each week in the Courier, who described the building as: *"a realisation of a great ambition' and a 'strikingly handsome building"*. Tours of the new hospital were arranged for the public at a cost of 2/6 for a daytime tour and 6d for an evening tour. Over 10,000 people took the chance to go around the hospital.

A special supplement was printed to celebrate the opening, calling the hospital 'a modern home of healing', and local suppliers were keen to publicise their involvement in the building. The supplement said the building had twelve refrigerators of the most modern kind.

The first patients, two small babies, were transferred to the new hospital on Saturday 11 August 1934 by the police and the St John Ambulance Brigade, who ran the only ambulance service in Tunbridge Wells at the time. Three weeks later patients were transferred from the Ear and Eye Hospital and the two hospitals were merged.

The Police Ambulance in Tunbridge Wells in 1934
© Photo courtesy of Kent Police Museum

Medical staff

Most of the medical staff and all consultants were honorary, and made a living from private contracts while providing unpaid support to the hospital. Dr Brian Hosford, one of the original medical staff at the Kent & Sussex Hospital, came across from the General Hospital. He left to join the Royal Army Medical Corps in 1939 and was at the evacuation of Dunkirk, where he was captured by German Forces and made a prisoner of war. He returned to the Kent & Sussex in 1945 and under the NHS became Lead Consultant Physician, retiring in 1970.

Another long-standing family of doctors were the Rankings. Dr John Ranking (1849-1912) was one of the first Honorary Consultants to the General Hospital. On his death, in a road accident an oak statue was made to commemorate his service to the hospital. It stood in the entrance hall of the Kent & Sussex Hospital and was moved to the Tunbridge Wells Hospital on opening.

His son, Bob, also became a physician at the General, moving to the Kent & Sussex as did his son, who died prematurely whilst on the Medical Staff in 1959, ending over 80 years of service from the family to Tunbridge Wells hospitals. The youngest of the Dr Rankings was a keen rower and competed for the country at the 1932 Los Angeles Olympic Games.

Dr John Cogan, a new ophthalmic consultant, was able to introduce a detached retina apparatus to the hospital. This was one of only two in the UK at the time, the other being at Moorfields in London.

The nurses' accommodation block, which cost £21,000, was opened a week later by Mr R. Burslem, who was the joint chairman of the two hospitals and chairman of the new hospital committee. Mr Burslem, an alderman, Mayor of Tunbridge Wells 1932-1934 and a magistrate, worked tirelessly to support the Tunbridge Wells Hospitals and after his death the block was named after him. Later, in 1938, an extension was opened after fundraising to increase the accommodation, in an age when all nurses lived in.

Another notable appeal fund was the Gutherie Memorial Fund, which raised money to equip one of the new operating theatres in memory of the late T.C. Gutherie, a surgeon at the old General Hospital. He arrived as a junior surgeon in 1902 having trained at St Thomas' Hospital in London.

Staff of the hospital just after opening

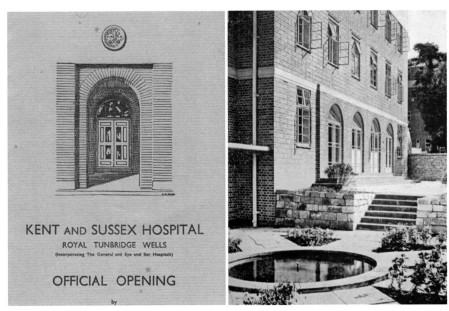

Official programme of the opening   *Garden of the Nurses' Home*

He was Honorary Surgeon to Dr Barnardo's Homes and on the Executive Committee of the British Medical Association. He spent much time and energy supporting the concept of a new hospital for Tunbridge Wells. However, he died at the young age of 60 in 1928 before his dream could be turned into reality.

Children's Ward

The old general hospital Children's Ward had a series of coloured tiles around the ward depicting nursery rhymes, and it was the intention to transfer them to the new hospital. Joseph Webb, the assistant secretary of the old hospital who had done so much to raise the money and get the site on Mount Ephraim, made plans to move the tiles to the new ward. Sadly he died suddenly in 1929 and it later proved impossible to move the tiles. The new ward would still have tiles though, and many patients remember the Children's Ward and the tiles, as they were in the ward for several weeks or months. One recalled being in the ward for ten weeks with a fractured femur and being pushed out into the garden in warm weather helped pass the time with a little enjoyment.

The inner quadrangle just prior to opening in 1934

Expansion

The first annual report in 1935 confirmed some 3,211 inpatients and nearly 10,000 outpatients had been seen. The hospital cost some £27,000 to run but income stood at only £24,544, resulting in a funding deficit of £3,000. This led to a concerted fundraising campaign.

The annual report from 1938 gives more details as to income, reporting legacies totalling over £2,000, church collections of nearly £1,000, payments from friendly societies of £7,500, from the Peanut Club of £600, and entertainments bringing in £1,000. The Annual Pound Day secured 15,000 eggs and 5,150 lbs of other goods from meat to vegetables.

The hospital received more royal visitors in 1936 when the Duke and Duchess of Kent toured the hospital and met patients and staff.

The work of the hospital continued in 1938, when over 7,000 X-rays were taken, 1,329 general operations conducted, 162 eye operations carried out and 1,455 dental operations carried out. In addition, a new radium room offering the latest cancer treatments was opened in 1937, expansion in various departments took place and beds were increased to 210.

*The new hospital Casualty and Outpatients Entrance –
the covered way to the Nurses Home is visible*

The front entrance and car park

*One of a series of postcards produced when the hospital opened.
The fire escape ramps are clearly visible in their sweeping and distinctive style*

The Poole Tiles

An appeal was launched and the Peanut Club raised considerable sums along with other donations to secure a new set of tiles made by Carter & Co from Poole. The design showed animals running down the ward to Noah's Ark along with several nursery rhyme characters was chosen. Each panel cost between £6 and £9 each and thanks to generous donations, the whole ward was tiled by the end of 1934. The Peanut Club also raised funds to buy a well stocked toy cupboard and lockers for each bed and cot. The tiles were painted over and boarded up in 1965 when the ward became an adult ward. It was not until 1984 that, through detective work, that the tiles were rediscovered for all to enjoy. When the Kent & Sussex Hospital closed, the tiles were removed by a specialist contractor and sold at auction. However, the unique and largest panel pictured below was saved and placed into the new hospital for all to enjoy.

Matron

The first Matron of the Kent & Sussex Hospital, May Kearsley, retired in 1938. Miss Kearsley became interested in nursing after seeing a man collapse in the street and she joined St John Ambulance, learnt first aid and nursing before beginning her nurse training at Manchester Royal Infirmary. In 1915, she moved to Sheffield and then, as Matron, to Tunbridge Wells General Hospital. In 1970 Dr Brian Hosford, one of the original doctors on the staff, recalled she was a: *"Matron of the old school and a strict disciplinarian".* After she left she married Alderman Burslem as his second wife, and continued to support the hospital.

Miss Kearsley was replaced by Mary Frere from St Bartholomew's Hospital in London, who was the first Ward Sister on Ward 9 at the Kent & Sussex Hospital, having been interviewed at the old General Hospital. She left to take up a Matron's post at the Australasia Hospital in Barking, Essex, before returning as Matron to the Kent & Sussex Hospital.

Mary Frere would stay at the hospital as a guiding force through traumas and changes for over 20 years.

The country was quietly preparing for war and the hospital spent £380 on air raid precautions work during 1938. The private beds at the hospital were a good income-generator for the hospital, with a single room costing £6 6s a week and shared double room costing £4 4s a week.

The hospital was up-to-date in every respect and in 1939 Viscount Nuffield gave the hospital an iron lung, used in the treatment of paralysis from polio. This modern invention enabled treatments to prolong life to be carried out at Tunbridge Wells for the first time. They were soon a common sight around both hospitals.

Visiting times were strict and children were not visited under any circumstances, while adult patients could be visited only between 1400 and 1530 on Wednesday and Sunday. This was later extended to Saturdays as well.

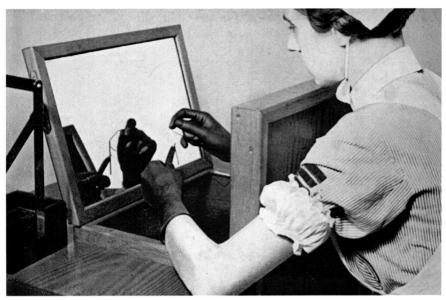

Radium needles being threaded for cancer treatment at the hospital in 1935

*Aerial view of the hospital in 1935 – its visibility from the air
would be a disadvantage in the war*

Ward _hai Surgical_   Under _Mr Nickett_

Ikent & Susser Ibospital,
ROYAL TUNBRIDGE WELLS.

Tel. 2380.

_29. 9_ 193_7_

A vacancy will be reserved on _Thursday 30th Sep_

for _Charles Tuckley Esq._

The patient must bring this card together with in-patient letter, Contributory Scheme or " Honey Comb " Scheme Voucher duly completed, and enter the Hospital at 2.30 p.m.   If the patient cannot come on the date named, please reply at once, so that the bed may be given to another patient.

O.P. No. _5330_

TOM B. HARRISON,
Superintendent-Secretary.

Patients insured under the National Health Insurance are particularly requested to fill in the following particulars before entering the Hospital :—

Name of Society _Independent Order of Odd Fellows_

Branch _Hand of Friendship_ Membership No. _58_

Name and Address of Local Agent or Secretary _Mr W Wilkins_
Langton Green

N.B.—Every patient must bring a proper change of clean body linen, soap, towel and tooth brush.

Admission cards for patients

It wasn't just nurses who were employed at the hospital - and Matron had total control over the entire domestic staff. The Matron's Log of the 1930s shows she employed several young girls including a ward maid age 14 on 12 shillings a week, a sewing room girl aged 15 on 7 shillings a week, Matron's maid aged 16 on £20 per year and a dining room maid aged 15 on £20 per year.

Many of these young girls were frequently needed at home to look after ill parents and left after a few years.

In 1937, the Sankey Report into Voluntary Hospitals recommended that nurses' hours be reduced from 118 per fortnight to 96. The hospital needed to employ an additional sister, 15 extra nurses and two maids, and to provide accommodation. Building costs were to be £10,500, which meant yet another appeal to the residents of Tunbridge Wells.

During 1937, the hospital spent £1,745 on meat, £1,277 on bread and had an occupancy of 188. There were 3,568 admissions in the year, with a length of stay of 19 days. The Casualty Department also saw 4,132 casualties.

The theatres were busy, too, with 1,263 general, 148 ophthalmic and 766 ENT operations being carried out.

An appeal to 'name a bed' was launched again, asking people to pay £1,000 to name a bed and £500 to name a cot for life. A new laundry opened in 1937, saving hundreds of pounds each year in washing bills. In its first week it processed over 10,000 items.

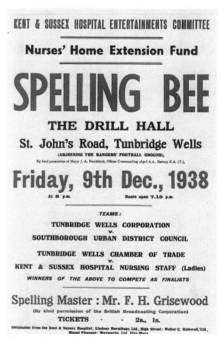

Donation receipt

Admission card

Form of agreement
signed by student nurses

Poster for spelling bee

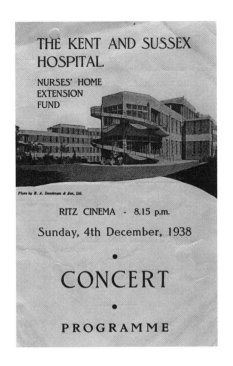

THE KENT AND SUSSEX HOSPITAL

NURSES' HOME
EXTENSION
FUND

Photo by E. A. Sweetman & Son, Ltd.

RITZ CINEMA - 8.15 p.m.

Sunday, 4th December, 1938

•

CONCERT

•

PROGRAMME

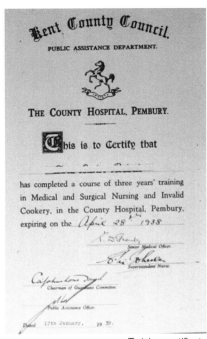

Kent County Council.

PUBLIC ASSISTANCE DEPARTMENT.

THE COUNTY HOSPITAL, PEMBURY.

This is to Certify that

has completed a course of three years' training in Medical and Surgical Nursing and Invalid Cookery, in the County Hospital, Pembury, expiring on the *April 28th 1938*

Senior Medical Officer.

Superintendent Nurse.

Chairman of Guardians Committee.

Public Assistance Officer.

Dated 17th January, 19 39.

Training certificate

Staff and children with Matron Kearsley on the Princess Elizabeth Children's Ward in 1937 – the Noah's Ark tiles can be seen on the back wall

83

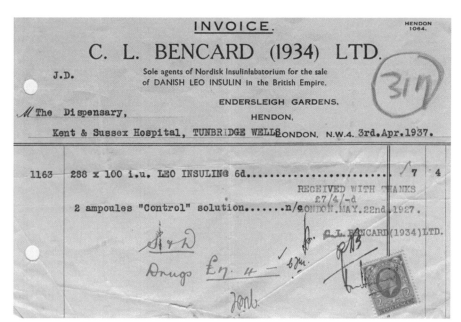

A receipt for drugs 1937

The Pembury Cedar Tree in heavy snow 1959

Chapter 5

Their Finest Hour...

The Second World War

As the country prepared for war between Britain and Germany, plans were being made by the Government to establish the Emergency Medical Service to manage the expected mass casualties from a war on the home front, as well as casualties from the fighting abroad. It required hospitals to work together for the national good, and they met the challenge head-on.

As early as 1935, plans were being made to evacuate hospitals into the countryside for more protection and to expand hospital capacity. The plans for South East England were being overseen by Professor T. B. Johnson from Guy's Hospital. Dr Grasby was called to Guy's Hospital in 1936 and told in the strictest confidence of the plans to make Pembury a Class 1A large base hospital in the event of war, and that his role would be as Medical Superintendent in Charge. The Executive Committee of the Kent & Sussex Hospital was also in discussion about its role as a Class 1A Emergency Hospital.

Throughout 1938, as the international situation escalated, the hospitals set up air raid precautions committees, blackout curtains were ordered, sand buckets collected and emergency lighting fitted. Gas masks arrived in parts for assembly and over 10,000 sandbags were ready for filling.

The Emergency Medical Service was based on a regional structure with the country divided up into sectors, each with a London teaching hospital at its heart. Tunbridge Wells fell into Sector Ten with Guy's Hospital.

Miss MacManus, Matron of Guy's Hospital, was appointed Sector Matron and set up her HQ at the County Council Hospital in Farnborough, with Professor Johnson as Sector Officer. Together, they set about organising the local hospitals and staffing. Later, the Sector HQ staff based themselves at Wildernesse, near Sevenoaks.

In September 1938, an order was given to stop all leave and halt all but emergency admissions in preparation for war. After Neville Chamberlain returned from Munich on the 30th of September citing *"peace in our time"* the situation eased, and the committees returned to normal business.

In the Spring of 1939, discussions were on going to construct wooden huts to expand emergency bed capacity at both hospitals. At Pembury, the steep slope made the project a real challenge, especially with the sandy soil structure. Dr Grasby had recommended that the huts be built at Pembury Grange nearby, which was being used for elderly care. Dr Grasby wrote:

"In due course contractors built foundations of large concrete floats on ground levelled on the slope, and with a period of rain the floats did in fact float down to the valley below! Undaunted, the Ministry found another firm of builders and built the 16 huts."

At the Kent & Sussex, the huts were built on the orchard behind the main hospital. Mr Fredrick B. Manser was appointed Medical Superintendent of the Hospital, after being brought out of retirement to lead the hospital through the war until his retirement in 1947. He was a popular choice, having started his hospital career in Tunbridge Wells during the First World War in 1918. His war would be a long one, with the responsibility of running the hospital and with the loss of his son whilst on active service abroad.

Mr FB Manser - Medical Superintendent at The Kent & Sussex

By the end of May 1939 the Emergency Committees at both hospitals had been re-established, and the Ministry of Health began to deliver emergency supplies. The Kent & Sussex received 205 mattresses, 205 bedsteads, 615 blankets and 410 pillows. Blackout preparations were complete at both hospitals by the end of August 1939, however, many areas had temporary blackouts or rooms out of bounds at night until it could be finished.

The increased capacity at Pembury meant a need to alter the sewage works, boiler house, canteen and many other facilities: *"So we were still in trouble but we prepared for war,"* noted Dr Grasby.

The Ministry sent all manner of equipment: *"I remember we were supplied a large number of green stretchers, some quite dreadful bedside lockers, and some hideous galvanised iron food trolleys which no self-respecting Sister would have allowed in her ward! The only use we put them to was to support glass tanks containing gold fish."*

The sites also constructed air raid shelters and gas decontamination rooms. Many of the air raid shelters at Pembury were in use as stores until 2011, when the site was demolished. Early in the war Frank Stanford started work as an apprentice painter at the hospital. He was given the task of painting the windows with black paint, as blackout material was in short supply: *"We painted many hundreds of windows but in the winter it meant no natural light inside, so lights had to be on 24 hours a day,"* he recalled. The blackout was total and the Pembury site was very dangerous, with absolutely no lights visible from outside and accidents were common.

Emergency

At 5 pm on Friday 25th August 1939, the hospitals were put on emergency standby by the Ministry of Health, and volunteers were drafted in to fill sandbags and assemble gas masks. The roof of the Kent & Sussex Hospital was covered in sand and netting with branches to camouflage the roof, and the white paint of the walls was painted dull army green and brown, mostly by volunteers. Sandbags and blast walls covered key areas at both hospitals, and at Pembury a large red cross adorned the top of the roof of the surgical block.

Volunteers fill sandbags outside the Board Room at the Kent & Sussex Hospital. Above can be seen the balcony of Matron's flat

On 1st September, the order was given to evacuate the hospitals, a task which at the Kent & Sussex was completed in just two hours. By 3rd September, when Neville Chamberlain announced the country was at war, all staff leave had been cancelled and all staff recalled for duty. At Pembury, the chapel service had been delayed for the 11 o'clock announcement on the radio, and the service was a sombre occasion. But the late summer sunshine drove people on and they were quickly ready to accept the challenge ahead.

*The Male Surgical Ward at Pembury (Addison Ward) 1938,
where SCBU would later be developed*

In addition, to changes in the hospitals, the county council was also expected to house and care for evacuees sent from maternity homes in more dangerous areas. Several emergency homes were opened to complement the Council's existing home in Calverley Park Gardens. These included homes opened at Broadwater Down and Romford House Farm in Pembury.

Pembury Hospital in 1937

Pembury Hospital in 1939

Pembury Hospital in 1945 showing wartime extensions

An air raid shelter at Pembury, used as a store until demolition

The Phoney War

The Phoney War, as it was called, produced very few casualties except, that is, for the increase in casualties from the blackout conditions imposed on the home front. Some people remember that the outbreak of war was greeted with an increase in admissions from people trying to commit suicide at the news that the country could expect gas attacks and heavy bombing within days. There is no hard evidence of this, although the theatre register at Pembury does show an operation for a patient with a cut throat on the 3rd of September, the day war was declared, but no such admissions were made at the Kent & Sussex. Dr Grasby remarked:

"It was a time of comparative peace –
certainly no signs of war as we
all settled down."

Dr Leedham recalled that at the start of the war most of the service sick were admitted from local army camps, where conditions were in his opinion *'appalling'*. In the first few weeks of 1940 over 170 were admitted following an epidemic of flu at the camps.

Pembury's finest hour

Soon after war was declared a convoy of doctors from Guy's Hospital arrived at Pembury, having been evacuated from London. They were to stay at Pembury for the duration of the war. Many of the staff arrived in double decker buses that drove into Pembury, taking down some of the internal phone lines as they arrived.

Dr Grasby recalled:
"140 Guy's students arrived at my office, each
bearing a chit signed by Professor Johnson saying
that in the event of hostilities they should report to
me at Pembury. I hadn't the slightest idea what to do with them!"

The dental and medical schools were eventually moved to Sherwood Park, a large house a few minutes from the hospital, and students billeted in houses around the town. The ever-resourceful schools used empty fruit lorries, taking fruit from Kent orchards to Borough Market, returning to Kent with teaching equipment and luggage. A full medical and dental school was opened on October 28th and continued until their return in 1944. The Dean reported that teaching facilities were *"most satisfactory"* in his report of December 29th 1939. Space was always a problem, and the empty Baptist Tabernacle was taken over in addition to other houses on the Pembury Road.

Although 500 young students living in Tunbridge Wells proved interesting, the authorities soon ensured they had plenty to do, such as forming a detachment of the Home Guard, fire watching and working for the Auxiliary Fire Service. There were many other roles to keep the students busy, including working as auxiliaries and orderlies on the wards at Pembury and the Kent & Sussex Hospital. A few also worked in various canteens for the Army, including the Canadian Forces stationed at Eridge Castle. Later a small school workshop was established, making small-scale precision items for armament contractors as part of the war effort.

Dr Bill Williams was a medical student from Guy's who was evacuated to Pembury. He remembers that in the event of war they were to report directly to Pembury. He was put up in tents on the lawn before finding lodging with a lady in Pembury village. During the first couple of years as a young student he remembers the fun of being in the country with not many lectures taking place. Other students recalled dissecting rabbits in the makeshift laboratories that were in the greenhouses, describing the consequences on hot days. During the Battle of Britain much time during lectures was spent looking out of the windows at the action rather than the subject in hand.

The nurses, some hundred of them, camped out in large tents on the lawn in front of 'B' Block and in the woods adjacent to the main canteen.

The Matron of Guy's, Miss Macmanus, recalled the fact that the tents were not of the strong army type needed and, whilst they enjoyed the summer, they: *"slept under umbrellas and ate in flapping darkness. The end surely arrived with the twirl of torn canvas and broken tent poles."*

There was much disquiet about the tents. Dr Grasby summed up the approach of the Sector Matron to this problem. 'Emily MacManus breezed through the hospital in her inimitable style as if no problem ever existed, and I heard her say to her girls enduring the inconvenience: *"My dears! There's a war on - didn't you know? We must make do! We lived in tents in the last war!"*

Reflecting on his experiences with the Sector Matron, Dr Grasby wrote: *"Emily McManus was an inspiration. She breathed confidence. Nothing to her was impossible and she was a born organiser. The association of Guy's and Pembury nurses could not have been more amicable and I think the nurses were happy. The Guy's nurses were, I suppose, theoretically under the aegis of our own Matron, Miss Fagelman, but I thought the integration was admirable and no problems occurred as far as I was concerned."*

As soon as possible, and with a great deal of support from Dr Jacoby, who spoke up for the nurses, they were moved into dormitories vacated by the workhouse, which although cramped were at least warm and dry.

The hospital management team consisted of Matron Fagelman, Dr Grasby and Jack Garrett the Steward, who met at 0930 daily to sort out the day. Dr Grasby remarked: *"We had many problems but we managed."*

The Paediatric Firm at Pembury in 1939:
Dr Jacoby is in the front row without a white coat

The need for another theatre was increasing and two side rooms in Amelia Scott Ward were pressed into service as a theatre in late 1940. Further building work took place, extending Woodlands House with canteen facilities. These remained canteens until taken over by Dietetics and the Functions Room.

The huts were a major fire risk, so across the site large static water tanks were constructed and staff were trained as fire fighters - even joining the Auxiliary Fire Service. This was just as well, as incendiary bombs were dropped on the site by German bombers in 1940, although all fires were put out quickly by the fire team. Dr Grasby remarked:

"Although we were in 'Bomb Alley' the hospital was never hit by anything big. We had lots of incendiary bombs dropped but many did not go off and were filled with sand! Bateup opened one up for me and there was a piece of paper inside saying 'from Czechoslovakia'. Those brave fellows duped the Germans at great risk to themselves."

1940 also saw the establishment of the first premature baby unit at Pembury under Dr Jacoby, making the Pembury Unit the third oldest outside London in the UK.

Dr Grasby turned his attention to the Radium supply: *"Another problem was what to do with the supply of radium. We thought of the hospital well some 30 feet deep and our engineer devised a device to lower it and the idea was that in a raid the needles could be removed and placed in a container in the well but it proved impractical. We finally had two huge steel containers made with a three inch cavity and steel thread enclosing it. If they were hit by a bomb then they would be blown intact without losing its lethal contents – we never used either of them!"*

HRH Princess Tsahai Selassie, the Emperor of Abyssinia's daughter, was training as a nurse in Guy's Hospital and evacuated to work at Pembury. The Matron of Guy's made strong representation to Miss Fagelman at Pembury for her to be moved to better quarters, as she was lodged in the old workhouse buildings with common wash areas. The Princess however wanted to be treated the same as everyone else whilst at Pembury, becoming a popular colleague.

HRH Princess Tsahai Selassie working at Pembury

The Battle of Britain

The sight of German planes being chased by Spitfires from the RAF was soon to become a common site as the Battle of Britain was fought in the skies over Tunbridge Wells.

In the *'History of Guys Hospital'* A.C. Cameron recalled: *"Planes, bullets or parts of planes showered from the sky, everywhere machine gun bullets ploughed their way into walls and asphalt paths."*

This view was echoed by Dr Grasby, who wrote:

"The Battle of Britain caused us much concern. We were right underneath it and bullets and shrapnel fell like rain. I was surprised by how hot these things were to pick up! But we had pilots who came down in parachutes and often were injured, with bullet wounds or fractures - and German pilots, too, shot out of the skies overhead. I always went to see any German as I had a smattering of German, and met one very young and terrified Luftwaffe pilot. He wore a magnificent uniform and was white with fear."

When I asked him in German what his name was he gave it at once - and where he came from and sundry bits of information that I am quite sure he never should have divulged but which was, I believe, useful to our Interrogation Officer."

Shrapnel poured down and low-trajectory anti-aircraft shells came perilously close and exploded overhead: *"We also had pilots of the Polish Squadron No.303. They were charming but impossible. I recall one of them saying to me when I saw him in the ward: 'Six days we fight – five German planes! POOH!' He was disgusted with his efforts. They were excellent pilots with one burning ambition: to kill the enemy, and they did. One English pilot I remember who suffered bullet wounds when his plane was badly hit. They brought his parachute to show what had brought him safely down. It was riddled with bullet holes and looked like fine lace and this brave fellow turned white when he saw it. How it brought him down safely is a mystery. Curious things did happen. I was standing outside my office one day when a Dornier 'pencil bomber' passed just above the gynealogical wards and crashed somewhere near the village. It went by completely silently with no engine noise, and I suppose may have been abandoned by the crew who had bailed out. It was an eerie experience."*

On one occasion, Frank Stanford was working on the roof of 'F' Block when three aircraft approached. Believing them to be local Spitfire squadrons the group waved to them. Quickly realising they were enemy Messerschmidt aircraft, they rapidly headed for the fire escape to get out of view: *"Not a shot was fired but it was a close call,"* he recalled. It was commonplace, especially in the Blitz, to see and hear the rows of German bombers heading into London over the hospital.

Dr Grasby had moved into the hospital for the duration with his family, and his daughter Janet recalled:

"I remember the throb of the bombers going overhead during the Blitz. I remember having nightmares that the hospital would burn down and look like the picture of the Blitz in the Illustrated London News, with flames pouring out of the windows."

Patients leave Guys Hospital in modified Greenline Coaches
Photo courtesy of the Imperial War Museum London

Dunkirk

In the summer of 1940, after the evacuation of the British Expeditionary Force from Dunkirk, the hospital saw many casualties who were evacuated from the coast by train. Casualties were brought from Tonbridge and Paddock Wood Stations by coach to the hospital. These soldiers were still wet from seawater, some with terrible injuries. Over 300 soldiers were admitted to Pembury. Many of those returning had considerable burns caused by the burning oil on the surface of the sea. The first casualties arrived on 28th May and the last arrived on 6th June. Twelve of those brought to Pembury from Dunkirk died despite the efforts of staff. The huts were pressed into use, with medical students commandeered to fit out the huts and work in the many convoys that shuttled between trains and the hospital.

In his post-war report Dr Grasby, who had been in charge at Pembury, said:

'I recall the courage and endurance of those patients and the supreme efforts of the staff.

Although we were not expected to admit many patients, as every effort was made to keep beds empty for the expected invasion, we had a large number, of all nationalities. One or two were exceptional.

I was called to a private room where a man had been admitted wearing a magnificent but unidentifiable uniform. I found he was a Belgian gendarme - very wet but unharmed. We had a Russian soldier, also uninjured, and we never found out his origin. He was a complete peasant and had never seen a water tap or a loo before. How does one explain the use of such things when one has no Russian? We never did.

More seriously, we had a group of French sailors, excellent fellows, who had been rescued at Dunkirk, taken aboard a destroyer and were on their way to England when their ship hit a mine which lifted the stern up a foot or two. The men were standing on deck and the explosion caused fractures of all their legs.

One French soldier, recovering from an anaesthetic, kept shouting "Ou est mon baton?" over and over again. It transpired that he had a murderous stick with which he intended to slay Germans. He quietened down after being given some sort of stick to hold.

They also brought with them every conceivable kind of weapon. We had to send Bateup, who knew about such things, to collect them and he ended up with buckets of ammunition, 303s and small arms, guns, pistols and revolvers, hand grenades and knives. We had to get soldiers to come and take them away."

The theatre register for the first three days in June 1940 shows nearly 40 soldiers a day were operated on in the two theatres, many with gunshot wounds but several needing amputations and more complex operations for shrapnel wounds.

Dr Leedham recalled that for three weeks emergency theatres had more than one table in at a time. Theatre 1 had three tables, Theatre 2, two tables and the new 'F' Block Theatre, two. In the morning after a night operating patients would be reassessed and moved on to Sevenoaks Railway Station, where hospital trains would convey them on to quieter parts of the country. Later, it was described by Dr Grasby as Pembury's 'finest hour'.

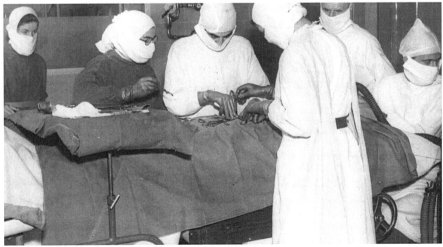

Operating Theatres at Pembury during the Dunkirk Emergency

On 9th October 1940 fifteen hop pickers were admitted to Pembury following an enemy attack at Beltring. This attack by German fighters, who machine gunned a group of Eastenders who were down for the hop picking season, saw ambulances back and forth to Beltring bringing severely wounded patients back. A two-year-old died, along with four other adult hop pickers.

Throughout 1940 and 1941 the hospital took in many civilian casualties from the local area after enemy action, including air raids.

Throughout the war years the theatre register shows many operations on servicemen for injuries in battle, but also many operations carried out on civilians for injuries on the home front, including removal of shrapnel. A dedicated orthopaedic theatre (Theatre 3) was opened in August 1943 in Hut 8, one of the Emergency Medical Service huts, together with dedicated orthopaedic wards in Huts 6,7,8,9 and 10. Huts 1, 2, 4 were given over to medical patients and Huts 3 and 5 were given over to surgical patients.

Military casualties wore a hospital uniform of a light blue jacket and trousers, white shirt and red tie, and they were well-known around the Pembury area. Later in the war casualties from the failed Allied raid on Dieppe arrived in the hospital, mostly Canadians.

Life for the staff was hard, especially with rationing, and the hospital gave nurses small plots of land on which to grow food. Ration books were kept in the general office where rations were dealt with to ensure staff were kept well-fed. Some nurses recall having their rations of butter, sugar and jam put into glass jars with their names on, written on pieces of elastoplast with a line to check that no one had been taking their rations.

The hospital had 1,100 beds and mattresses at the start of the war, with beds and mattresses in every corner of the hospital.

As the bombing raids in the towns and cities became more concentrated and dangerous during 1940, hospitals across the east coast of Kent were evacuated to safer parts of the country. This included the Kent & Canterbury Hospital, which was moved to Pembury overnight before patients were moved on to safer areas in the West Country. Dr Grasby recalled:

"With the reverses in France we were called upon to house, temporarily, in our empty huts, displaced persons, mostly old, from the Dover area. I remember converted buses arriving at the hospital gates and our team of porters, under Bateup, an ex RSM, lifting hundreds of green stretchers or helping aged people into the wards. It was a Herculean task and I never knew how they managed it, especially as those same porters put them into similar Green Line buses the next day for their journey to the safety of Wales."

On 23rd June 120 patients arrived, followed by 20 TB patients the day after, but this was only the prelude to 28th June when over 400 evacuees arrived, and 7th July when 180 arrived.

The Orthopaedic Unit started in 1939 with the move to Pembury from Guy's Hospital of Mr Constantine Lambrinudi, a world-famous consultant orthopaedic surgeon. He was known for his rather left-wing views, and caused concern amongst War Office officials by distributing copies of the 'Daily Worker'. They saw it as subversive propaganda and it was eventually banned.

He suffered from ill health and often did only the complicated part of operations, allowing others to open and close. Although unwell he was often seen on the ward floor demonstrating exercises to patients. His premature death in 1943 was felt around the country.

His replacement, Mr John Mayer, then went on to develop the unit with its own theatre through the advent of the NHS, with orthopaedics as a speciality. John Mayer was another Guy's Hospital man, who had worked during the war in the Army Medical Corps in Egypt and Africa, even being mentioned in despatches at the Battle of El Alamein.

His appointment to Pembury marked a move to provide a permanent specialist orthopaedic service at Pembury. He saw that the way to influence change was to be at the heart of it, and served on both the Tunbridge Wells Hospital Management Committee and the South East Thames Regional Hospital Board.

The end of the workhouse forever

The workhouse was formally closed in 1941, and the Master and Matron there pensioned off so the buildings could be pressed into war service. The last Master and Matron were Mr and Mrs Partridge.

"The Partridges were the most charming and pleasant people who I spent many happy hours with – he was a splendid administrator,"

recalled Dr Grasby. The hospital passed from the Public Assistance Committee into the care of the Public Health Committee of Kent County Council on July 1st 1941, and became a whole-time hospital. An American 'lend lease' ambulance was based at Pembury from January 1942.

Admissions to the Pembury Hospital increased from 2,057 in 1938 to 5,424 in 1941. Beds decreased slightly by 1943 to 750, and still further to 564 beds in 1945. This was mainly as some of the huts were converted into accommodation for nurses, and the development of the radiotherapy department in 'B' Block, where wards above were converted into accommodation and treatment areas modified downstairs. The cost to the council was significant, with the cost of the hospital increasing from £57,894 in 1938 to a huge £242,353 in 1948.

The dangers of explosives were publicised by the coroner after he conducted an inquest at Pembury in 1943, after a 12-year-old died after collecting shells and bullets causing an explosion.

Entertainments for the huge amount of staff and patients on site were often written and organised by Dr Grasby, in addition to the ENSA (Entertainments National Service Association) concerts and dances which were fondly remembered by the staff who lived there. The fetes were well attended, raising money for the Red Cross or other causes. Staff worked hard making all manner of things to sell on stalls. With materials in short supply nurses used their initiative to jazz up existing clothes for the dances.

Frank Stanford recalled: *"Nurses asked if I had silver paint - and we did as it was used on pipes. So I ended up painting many nurses' shoes silver, until my boss found out I was charging 6d a pair. I had to give their money back!"*

Dr Grasby's daughter Janet recalled: *"I made a huge teddy bear out of an old blanket and was so proud when Lady Abergavenny bought it and, in her splendid uniform as something very grand in the Red Cross, carried it around with her for the whole afternoon. There were splendid sideshows. One of the most popular was tipping a pretty nurse out of bed. This bed was contrived by the engineers to tip when a ball was thrown at a target and hit the bull's-eye."*

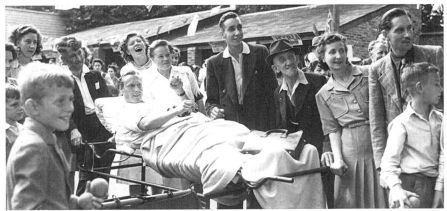

A soldier at the Pembury Fete

Pembury Fete during the war - The Bulls-Eye Bed Game

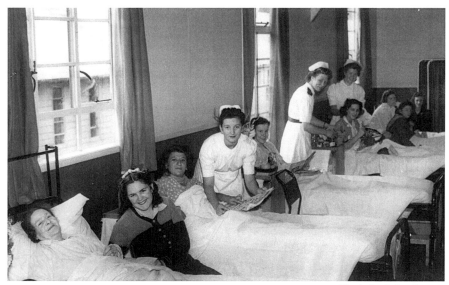

The huts during the war

Catering for such large numbers of people was a huge task. Staff and gardeners turned as much land as possible into garden plots to grow vegetables and fruit to supplement the rationing that was in force. The task of keeping everyone fed fell to Dorothy Dunnett, the Catering Officer, who ran the catering operation from the old workhouse kitchens with a team of staff.

Phyllis Chandler started in the kitchens at Pembury as a 14-year-old in the war, and recalled the mammoth task of peeling hundreds of potatoes each day. Piles of whatever other vegetables could be sourced had to be prepared and then steamed.

"In the afternoons we had cleaning to do, scrubbing the big food preparation blocks, often watched very carefully by Dorothy Dunnett who made sure the place was spotless. It was very hard work. It always seemed so cold and wet." She recalled how everything was made fresh daily, including custard, but that because of the space, fish and chips was served on a rota basis around the wards as they couldn't cook enough fish for everyone!

Rationing caused all sorts of logistical nightmares. Phyllis Chandler recalled: *"We got hold of whale meat once and cooked it up with onions and carrots, but it really wasn't popular!"*

Wartime Matron, Miss Fagelman, had her dinner cooked and served separately. Phyllis Chandler recalled: *"She was a little lady, but always very smart and she had total respect – I was always scared of cooking her dinner!"* On one occasion she cooked a milk junket for pudding but put too much junket in, making it rancid. She was summoned to the Catering Officer to explain herself, and Matron sent the offending pudding over for her to try.

Frank Stanford recalled:

"Matron was feared but fair, and I was summoned to see her several times. After knocking out a ward sister with a bowling ball he was summoned but after making him sweat she simply told him: *"In life we learn by our mistakes."*

As the war, went on Phyllis Chandler remembers the 'Boys in Blue', wounded troops in blue uniforms they wore around the hospital, who would often pop their heads into the kitchen for a chat. *"Of course we had Guy's Hospital nurses', too – they wore such beautiful uniforms."*

Flying bombs

Later in the war the hospital was made ready as a casualty clearing station for the D Day landings, but this plan was changed following the increase in V1, (doodlebugs), and V2 flying bombs that were falling across the South East causing terrible damage.

The hospital saw many casualties from flying bombs, especially the Lewisham incident where many died in July 1944 when a flying bomb landed on a shelter in the market area. Dr Grasby reported at the end of the war:
"It is a miracle that the hospital escaped serious damage."

He recalled:
"The first doodle bomb to pass over us we thought was typically German. I said to Garrett who was with me that it made such a vulgar sound! These wretched things passed over us, but some were brought down by fighter planes and careered all over the sky before coming down, but not on us.

The V2 rockets, I thought, were the most fiendish and revolting weapons ever conceived - and I remember the young girls from the Lewisham bomb, which caused so many facial injuries from flying glass, being brought to our wards. The medical students saw plenty of bomb damage."

The total number of civilian casualties admitted was almost as great as the total number admitted in the other five years of war. He reflected on the different nature of these casualties: *"These sad cases were mostly young people, many of whom sustained disfiguring scars and lacerations of their faces."*

Dr Grasby's daughter Janet recalled: *"The weather was gorgeous and we used to hang out of the windows watching the RAF flying alongside the doodlebugs and tipping their wings to put them off course. It was extremely exciting!"*

In July 1940, a triple murder at nearby Matfield brought a distraction from the war. Three bodies brought to the hospital mortuary and post mortems being carried out by the famous Home Office Pathologist Sir Bernard Spilsbury gave students a rare chance to see his work close up. The case made national headlines and was investigated by the Metropolitan Police Flying Squad.

The hospital had a constant stream of high-profile visitors in the war, including the Minister of Health Malcolm MacDonald and Dr Godber, later to become the Chief Medical Officer, who had been brought in as an inspector of the Emergency Medical Service in 1939. Janet recalled: *"We met our first Bishop, who was the Bishop of Rochester, dressed in frock coat and gaiters. We didn't know whether to kneel down and kiss his ring!"*

The hospital, with its increase in population, also attracted attention from criminals and in 1941 four women were fined and two were imprisoned after thefts of food and clothing from the hospital.

The chapel played a key role in hospital life in the war and the hospital's first chaplain was Eric Wells, father of the comedian John Wells.

Dr Grasby recalled: *"He was a great character, kind and helpful, and did the patients a lot of good when he talked to them of their injuries and worries. He preached valuable sermons, full of humour. We used to attend the services with nurses and some patients in the hospital chapel, a small Victorian building. Mr Garrett and I always read the lessons, and quite often Mrs Garret would sing an anthem.*

Many patients had spinal or bone injuries which meant they lay on their backs in plaster beds. We thought it would be easier for the nurses if we removed the metal mesh from the green stretchers and incorporated the plaster bed into it. In this way the patient could be easily moved on the trolley wheels and, with a front plaster, he could be turned over with comparative ease.

"It occurred to me that some of these patients could be taken in our ambulance to the chapel, and the metal stretchers place over the pews. The idea was well received and I got Bateup and his men to do it, which they did entirely voluntarily. To see these patients covering the middle of the chapel, singing their heads off in full and ample voice, and hear them laugh at Eric Wells' cheerful sallies, was a joy in itself".

The beginning of the end

After the initial rush of Dunkirk, the Blitz and the Battle of Britain, Pembury was able to resume normal business. Dr Grasby pointed out: *"The wards were filled with normal admissions of sick people and cold surgery, and we were very busy. The maternity unit was as busy as in peace time. We did have more war casualties, of course, and many unhappy people transferred from London Hospitals."*

As the war grew to an end, several huts vacated by Guy's Hospital were turned into nurses' accommodation. These huts were cold - as one nurse recounts, the face flannels were often frozen to the basin in the morning.

In 1945, a large house called Blackhurst was purchased and put into use as a preliminary training school for nurses. This house was used for many years and has fond memories for many student nurses in Tunbridge Wells. Beryl Whiddett started her training at Blackhurst in 1947 with students from Folkestone Hospital. She was told at the start of her training by Lady Abergavenny that they would enjoy a new hospital by the end of their training – something that would take much longer to come to pass.

The end of the war also saw investment in the hospital, with a grant of £11,500 for new equipment and £1,380 for beds to replace the wartime-issue wooden ones.

The end of the ENSA concerts saw the hospital bring a mobile cinema to entertain the staff and patients. At the start of 1945, 216 nurses were housed in the wooden huts.

The end of hostilities also saw the deep X-ray apparatus, brought down from London to Sherwood Park in the war, installed at Pembury in 'B' block, starting the County Cancer Centre. Towards the end of 1945, four huts were released by the Emergency Medical Service and pressed into service for KCC to care for TB patients, with concrete verandas built to enable patients to be in the fresh air.

On return to Pembury after coming out of the Army, Frank Stanford started to see the hospital return to normality. His first job was scraping off the black paint from the windows he had painted during the start of the war.

Dr Grasby summed up in 1946: *"During the war years it is a pleasure for me to report the great help we have had from the sector and from Guy's, and to record the spirit of co-operation which has existed between our two hospitals. It cannot be denied that we have benefited enormously from our association with Guy's, and we would like to think that this will continue in any future hospital service."*

In all, 14 members of HM Forces died at Pembury. along with two French soldiers and a Polish pilot.

Some famous faces worked at Pembury, especially during the war years, including:

Winifred Mary Ward (1884 – 1975), pioneer of speech therapy.

Hermann Lehmann (1910 – 1985), pathologist, expert in sickle cell disease.

Earnest Cranmer Hughes OBE (1878 – 1950), renowned teacher of surgery.

George Enderby (1915 – 2003), pioneer of hypotensive anaesthetics, where blood pressure was lowered to reduce bleeding.

Norman Jacoby (1911 – 1994), paediatrician who revolutionised the management of children in hospital.

Dr A.A. Osman, pioneering renal physician, who established the first renal unit at Pembury. He was known around Pembury as the Wizard of Oz.

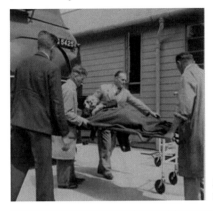

Patients arrive at Pembury having been evacuated from the coast

Dr Norman Jacoby (1911 - 1994)

Born in Johannesburg in South Africa in 1911, he was educated at Park Town andafter a long sea voyage joined the Medical School at Guy's Hospital.

In 1939 he was a Registrar at Guy's and transferred to Pembury with the Emergency Medical Service as a consultant. Although the only paediatrician between the coast and London, he also gave anaesthetics during the Dunkirk Emergency at Pembury.

In 1949 his unit at Pembury was the first in England to have unrestricted visiting by parents. He understood children as he was on their wavelength. Visiting was often restricted to once a week on children's wards, but he thought this cruel and emotionally damaging. So he and legendary ward sister Anne Bowley discussed how often parents should be able to visit. They quickly concluded that unrestricted visiting was the only solution. His commitment and vision saw the first Special Care Baby Unit established at Pembury, only the third outside London.

His view of tonsillectomy in children was legendary. He once wrote: "Children under my care had tonsillectomies over my dead body!" He pioneered the use of Rammstedts Operation under local anaesthetic, saving transfer to London.

He was a pioneer and a motivator and a naturally gifted clinician. He believed that practising medicine is not a job but a privilege

With thanks to Michael, Robin, Richard and James Jacoby

Matron Fagelman and new PTS entrants at Pembury 1943

Kent & Sussex Hospital's war

At the Kent & Sussex Hospital, too, wartime service was hard and every bit of space was made over to the war effort, including the Board Room, which was kitted out with beds. One nurse remarked that the service casualties ruined the floor with their 'clumsy boots'.

The first war casualties were those in the Army based at camps nearby, but the first air raid casualty arrived on July 17th 1940 when two casualties were brought in after an air raid. Throughout 1940 casualties from air raids and the Battle of Britain kept the Casualty Department busy. During the Battle of Britain casualties from shrapnel and machine gun bullets came in, along with two German pilots shot down.

Between July 1940 and December 1940, the Casualty Department saw 47 air raid casualties. Most of the pilots shot down and treated at the Kent & Sussex were very young - the oldest was just 24 years old.

In a routine visit by members of the Executive Committee to the Kent & Sussex in 1940 they reported:

"Our visit coincided with the air raid siren. The precautions taken seemed adequate and all personnel appeared to know their duties to carry out in a quiet and orderly manner."

The hospital, which was very visible from the air, was quickly camouflaged with bushes and paint and a quantity of sand over the roof. The Kent & Sussex, too, had air raid shelters and a gas decontamination room installed, along with blast walls and sandbags. It also housed the town's main First Aid Post. All the windows were painted with shatterproof film to prevent glass shattering.

The camouflage did cause concern, however, as a fire broke out in netting outside the Children's Ward in 1941, and the roof began to leak where stagnant water had built up on the roof under the sand. At the end of the war the Courier published a map showing the concentration of bombs that fell, and it showed the area around the hospital to be one of the most heavily bombed parts of Tunbridge Wells.

It was on 12th September 1940, during a heavy raid that the Kent & Sussex was bombed. After a string of bombs fell across the site one exploded in the Outpatients Department near Casualty and another in the forecourt. Sadly, Lincoln Redman, an 11-year-old boy delivering newspapers, died in the raid and several others required hospital treatment.

Pictures were taken by the War Office and the Ministry of Information as propaganda photographs. Even the Courier could not report the target as the Kent & Sussex Hospital due to wartime censorship restrictions, referring to it as 'a hospital in South East England'.

It was also in 1941 that a preliminary nurse training school was established at the Kent & Sussex, where student nurses did two months with a sister tutor in the classroom before starting their three-year training course around the wards.

Bomb damage to the Outpatients Department in 1940
Photo courtesy of the Imperial War Museum London

In 1941, the Kent & Sussex had 534 beds and admitted over 5,000 inpatients during the year, at an average cost of three pounds six shillings and sixpence a week. Later, in 1942, the massage department was moved into the huts, allowing a fracture theatre and clinic to be developed as part of the war effort. The Government gave the hospital a contribution for treating war casualties, and in 1942 this was £36,487 - nearly half the income for the hospital, whose drug bill was £3,654 during the year.

Val Harrison was a patient in the Princess Elizabeth Children's Ward between July 1940 and Christmas 1941, and spent most of her time in traction.
The beds were pulled away from the windows during air raid alerts, but due to her traction she had to be nursed in the corridor outside Sister's office for most of the time during which air raids were a risk. She recalled:

"We had wounded soldiers in the ward upstairs who used to come down, but they were banned from bringing us sweets and these had to be given to Sister. The staff were lovely."

The preparation for rounds by Matron and the doctors stuck in her mind: *"There was a lot of rushing around and we were warned to make sure we kept our beds tidy."*

During 1942 the hospital treated 5,832 inpatients and had over 92,000 outpatient attendances. The failed allied raid on Dieppe meant the huts soon became full of wounded Canadian soldiers injured in the attack. The huts, which until then had not been fully utilised, were at once full to overflowing. The huts became known for many years as the Canadian Huts.

At the height of the war Aunt Agatha wrote to Peanut Club members with reassuring words: *"Autumn berries are already thick in the hedges and squirrels scurry amongst the leaves, laying in their store of nuts for days to come. We will lay in our store of memories, and not all the air raids in the world shall rob us of them. Don't be afraid. No height or depth of fortune, not even the tragedy of war, can wrest it from us."*

A number of foreign nurses and radiographers worked at the hospital during this period. However, the Government, fearful of spies, soon wrote to Matron asking for guarantees that these staff - referred to as 'aliens' - would not come into contact with HM Forces. As a result the nurses were confined to the Children's Ward, and the radiographers asked to leave.

It was impossible under wartime rationing to hold Pound Days, but in May 1943 much-needed money was donated after a Flower Day, when nearly £270 was donated. The financial situation was causing concern in 1943, when the public were keen to give what little was spare to war causes. Mr Burslem addressed the issue in the Courier when he revealed that activity had increased by 33% since 1938, but funding had gone down.

The increase in casualties from all over the country led the Executive Committee to open the hospital on Saturdays for extra visiting, in January 1944. The first real signs of the start of the NHS appeared in a government white paper in February 1944 called 'A National Health Service'. It estimated the costs would be £132m, with £40m running costs a year.

With D Day imminent in 1944 the Government issued instructions that only emergency and urgent cases be admitted. The hospital took 14,428 X-rays and gave 44,567 massage treatments and 151 radium treatments. It saw 994 medical patients, 3,031 surgical patients and 49 maternity cases in 1944.

1944 saw a surge in casualties from the home front as the flying bombs wreaked havoc across South East England. The worst day was 17th June 1944, when 13 casualties from flying bomb attacks were admitted. Another 24 would follow before the war finished. Kent County Council agreed to buy Sherwood Park, which was in use by Guy's Hospital Medical School, for use by Pembury Hospital for £16,000.

The impending peace was a chance to get more donations, and adverts appeared encouraging people to give peace donations to the hospital.

Life remained hard even after hostilities had ceased, and rationing became stricter than in the war. In 1946 the nurses complained to Matron Frere at the Kent & Sussex Hospital about the food: "*Is it possible for the dietician to arrange fewer potato-less days, as on these days nurses are leaving the dining room still feeling hungry?*"

In reply, Matron wrote: "*THERE ARE NO POTATO-LESS DAYS - there are just potato-less meals. The hospital used to buy one ton and 8cwt of potatoes a week and now, due to rationing, receives only 9.5 cwt of potatoes a week. I would like to point out how very sorry the hospital authorities are that potatoes should be cut, but until rations are increased it is absolutely impossible to give you more.*"

In 1945 restrictions on admissions were lifted and things started to get back to a kind of normality. At the end of the war the Kent & Sussex Hospital had admitted 6,467 services patients and seen almost 18,000 as outpatients.

The financial situation was dire and constant appeals were made to plug the gaps. At the end of December 1944 the Courier revealed income in the previous nine months was £55,500, but expenditure was over £70,000. By April 1945 the hospital was overspent by nearly £10,000. Cinema shows, appeals and an SOS in the Courier saw money pour in during Kent & Sussex Benefit Week in November 1945.

By the time VE Day arrived six Allied servicemen and a German pilot shot down had died at the Kent & Sussex Hospital.

The miracle of Penicillin

John Cogan, a long-standing consultant eye surgeon, described in 1970, after his retirement, the introduction of Penicillin. It was reserved for military casualties. He recalled that the first dose of Penicillin was obtained from an American Army base at Rusthall, which he gave to a National Fire Service worker with an infection. The swelling and infection started to go down within 24 hours but the US then realised it was not for a member of the forces and withdrew supply. The patient died from the infection while being transferred to London.

In January 1945, the Courier headline shouted 'Amazing results of Penicillin – remarkable recoveries at the Kent & Sussex Hospital'. It featured the first few civilian uses of the antibiotic, including treatment for a five-year-old boy with severe burns that became infected, and a girl with infection in her bones that previously would have led to amputations or even death. A special appeal was set up to buy more of this wonder drug for use in Tunbridge Wells. It raised £844 in just two months.

Nurses

Towards the end of the war, the issue of nurses marrying was discussed by the Executive Committee. A nurse called to request special leave as her fiancé was on embarkation leave. Matron asked for advice from the Nursing Committee. They replied that nurses could marry but 'could not as a right expect it'. Later a Sister got married and asked to live out and remain a Sister. Matron advised the Committee it was 'unwise' to employ a married Sister and therefore she was asked to resign.

Victory

Restrictions on admissions would have to made for another reason - and that was lack of staff. The sense of relief was evident as nurses made comments in Ward Report Books such as that for Women's Medical at Pembury. The top page is neatly adorned 'VE Day +1!'

Dr Grasby's daughter Janet recalled: *"I remember VE Day and dancing around the bonfire below the nurses' home, watching the sparks go high into the air and not having to worry about the blackout."*

Nurses from both Pembury and Kent & Sussex took part in the Victory Parade on 8th June with other nurses from across Kent. The nurses from across the county were marshalled in Tunbridge Wells and sent by train to London, where they paraded in front of the King and Queen, Queen Mary and Winston Churchill before enjoying a firework display in Hyde Park.

The Rushcliffe Committee recommended that nurses should receive a pay rise and this was accepted by the Government, meaning a Ward Sister's salary rose to £160 a year plus accommodation, meals and uniform.

As the hospitals came out of World War Two there was a mixture of the old and the new. Life wouldn't be the same again - but some things remained the same for now!

Dorothy Wheeler recalled: *"Matron did her rounds and visited every ward. The wheels of the beds had to face down the ward, the pillowcases had openings away from the door, and all patients had to be in bed and tidy.*

"The lockers had to be washed and polished, and a jug and clean glass on top. Flowers had to removed at night and brought back in the morning with fresh water."

Another nurse recalled being summoned to Matron's office: *"You always had to wear a hat, and she was always called 'Matron' - and I was usually clutching a shilling to replace another broken thermometer!"*

Nurses on the Children's Ward at the Kent & Sussex Hospital, in front of windows taped up to prevent flying glass from bomb blasts

Wartime Entertainment at Pembury during 1943

THIS

CERTIFICATE OF HONOUR

IS AWARDED TO

Pembury Hospital

SAVINGS GROUPS

IN RECOGNITION OF SPECIAL ACHIEVEMENT

DURING THE

WINGS FOR VICTORY

NATIONAL SAVINGS CAMPAIGN 1943

I EXTEND MY THANKS TO ALL CONCERNED
IN THIS IMPORTANT NATIONAL SERVICE.

Archibald Sinclair

SECRETARY OF STATE FOR AIR

The Great Triumvirate – the management team at Pembury during the war, VE day celebrations: Matron Fagelman, Medical Superintendent Grasby and Steward Garrett

Nurses at the Kent & Sussex Hospital posing next to grass dug up for vegetables during the war

Chapter 6

From the cradle to the grave:
the NHS begins 1948 - 1958

The return to normality

At the end of the war conditions were tough, thanks to rationing, unemployment, bomb damage and sheer exhaustion. The rationing system got harder before it got better, and the age of austerity would have to continue for several years. The idea of a welfare state, with its universal access and benefits, had been proposed in the Beveridge Report, and after the war it became a reality.

The King's Fund reported, in 1945, that there was uneven distribution of hospital facilities, with no arrangements for ensuring existing buildings were used to best advantage. There were a number of small uneconomic hospitals and clinics, with many voluntary hospitals running parallel with local authority hospitals and providing duplicated services. Indeed in Tunbridge Wells this was just the case. They proposed a regional approach, linking with a large teaching hospital along the lines of that set up under the Emergency Medical Service. Many hospital buildings, including those at Tunbridge Wells, were damaged by bombing and needed significant expenditure to repair.

The National Health Service Act 1946 proposed a nationalisation of hospitals and a free-at-point-of-use health service for all. It was Health Minister Aneurin Bevan who used the phrase 'from the cradle to the grave' to describe his vision. He had also passionately described his 'big five giants', citing poverty, disease, ignorance, squalor and idleness as obstructions on the road to reconstruction after the war, with the welfare state as the answer. It was not going to be easy and the medical profession, especially the British Medical Association (BMA), were initially hostile. The Bill received an unprecedented fourth reading, and Bevan himself gave a speech reminding MPs that 'parliament ran the country not the BMA'.

The idea of the NHS was first discussed at the hospitals in March 1946. The Executive Committee at the Kent & Sussex Hospital was not overly enthusiastic about it. It was 'prepared to play its part provided that their independence was preserved. This hospital could not agree to complete nationalisation of the hospitals'.

So strong was the feeling that they lobbied the local MP: *"We express concern at the possibility of nationalisation of the hospitals (and) hope that as MP you will do everything you can to retain the independence of the ... hospitals,"* they wrote. The Courier avidly reported the local meetings and the objections to the NHS by the medical staff and the Executive Committee.

THE COURIER.

They Think Act Needs Amending

DOCTORS HOSTILE TO HEALTH BILL

Resolve To Act In Line With B.M.A. Attitude

"Courier" 29.3.46

DOCTORS AND NEW HEALTH BILL

"NOT ENTHUSIASTIC" IN TUNBRIDGE WELLS

"Courier" 12.4.46

"The Biggest Act Of Brigandage Since Henry VIII."

Hospital Chairman Speaks Out On National Health Bill

At Pembury, however, there was much support for the idea, as they were in effect already a public hospital funded by Kent County Council. Dr Grasby had long supported the concept of a National Health Service, having seen the appalling suffering in London whilst at Guy's in the 1920s, and firmly believed that no-one should be penalised for being ill. Consultants at Pembury, many from Guy's, were keen to develop their specialist services in the area with the new NHS and avidly supported its concept.

In April 1946 Mr Burslem, as chairman of the Kent & Sussex Hospital Committee, spoke at a public meeting saying: *"Hospital efficiency will not be improved by grabbing the gifts of the past donors and spurning those of today!'*

He later went further by accusing the Government of *"the biggest act of brigandage since Henry VIII took over the monasteries!"*

His objection ended by accusing the Ministry of 'robbery of the dead' by using legacies intended for local hospitals. They feared that funds raised by local people would be taken away and used to support poorer areas.

Meanwhile daily life was still tough and Matron Frere had constant complaints about uniforms and food at the Kent & Sussex. In June 1946 the Staff Nurses formally complained about lack of variety and the way in which food was cooked. Rationing of material meant a shortage of uniforms for new staff. Steadily, services staff returned to their units and others were demobbed, others left the district and a shortage of nurses led to bed closures. Wards were closed at Kent & Sussex and Pembury during 1946 and 1947 owing to a serious shortage of nursing staff.

In March 1947, the hospital took the unusual step of broadcasting an appeal on BBC Radio after the news. They asked for help in finding a dose of a new antibiotic called Streptomycin for a six-year-old boy seriously ill at the hospital. A dose was located and flown to Tunbridge Wells from the United States. The Courier reported the successful use of this 'wonder drug'.

During 1947, the rules on living out were relaxed and from then all but ENT and theatre nurses could live out.

At Pembury, the legacy of the war and its close relationship with Guy's led to the opening of a radiotherapy unit as a joint venture with Guy's Hospital. Thirty six beds were staffed by Guy's as their department in London had been damaged by bombs. Although staff returned in 1949 the unit was able to be reopened with local staff by 1951.

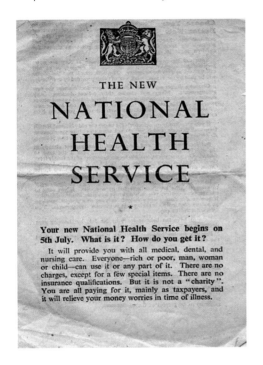

In 1948, the Kent & Sussex Hospital produced its last annual report, saying: *"It is with deep regret that the executive committee concludes that this is the last report of the Kent & Sussex Hospital as a voluntary hospital. It is hoped that despite state ownership, local interest will continue."*

The comment from one of the committee ended 'Red tape instead of nurses!'

To commemorate the Kent & Sussex Hospital and the handover to the Ministry of Health, a stone plaque was installed in the entrance hall by the Abergavenny and Camden families, who had taken a lead in helping the hospitals since 1828. At the closure of the Kent & Sussex Hospital this was moved to the new Tunbridge Wells Hospital.

Nurse Prize Giving at Kent & Sussex Hospital

The Designated Day

The Designated Day was 5th July 1948, when all voluntary hospitals and local authority hospital buildings were taken over by the new NHS. The Peanut Club closed down the week before the NHS started, having raised over £84,000 for the hospital and recruiting over 216,000 members. A branch carried on in East Grinstead to support the Children's Ward, which was named Peanut Ward.

Each area was divided up into Hospital Management Committees, and Tunbridge Wells hospitals were managed by the Tunbridge Wells Group Hospital Management Committee. Its new chairman was Mr Burslem, former chairman of the Kent & Sussex Hospital Committee. Each Group reported to a regional board and in Kent it was the South East Metropolitan Hospital Board. Mr Burslem also sat on this board. Ambulance Services, School Health and other parts of the health service were to be the responsibility of the Health Department of the County Councils. The Tunbridge Wells Committee initially met at the Kent & Sussex Hospital but quickly moved into new offices at Sherwood Park, recently vacated by Guy's Hospital after the war.

The Tunbridge Wells Group included:

Kent & Sussex Hospital	Pembury Hospital
Tonbridge Cottage Hospital	Queen Victoria Hospital East Grinstead
Homeopathic Hospital	Edenbridge Hospital
Hawkhurst Hospital	Crowborough Hospital
Capel Isolation Hospital	Cranbrook & Tenterden Isolation Hospital
Tunbridge Wells Smallpox Hospital	Hospital Tunbridge Wells Isolation
Broadwater Down Maternity Home	Northfield Maternity Home
Tunbridge Wells Maternity Home	Cranbrook Convalescent Home
Rusthall Grange Nursery	David Salomon's House

Most of these were owned by voluntary and charity groups or were established in the war and taken over by the NHS in 1948. The group also took ownership of the two TB dispensaries in Tunbridge Wells and Tonbridge. Each hospital had a house committee and at Pembury Dr Grasby chaired this committee, having resigned as Medical Superintendent and reverted to Consultant Gynaecologist and Obstetrician. His opinions of management by committee were well known. He wrote: *"Two observations I found fully confirmed. "A committee takes minutes and wastes hours" and "A camel must have been put together by a committee". The things we spent hours on were the sort of problems that Matron, Jack Garrett and I would have dealt with at our normal morning sessions in my office. There's much to be said for a benevolent dictator!"* At the first meeting of the Tunbridge Wells Management Committee Mr Burslem as chair stated: *"The change has gone very smoothly and so far as the public is concerned they have not had anything to complain about."*

Local dentists still refused to be part of the NHS, and patients were advised to go to the nearest casualty department for nearly two years after the formation of the NHS.

The most immediate effect was the rise in salaries and standard terms and conditions of the staff. However at Kent & Sussex Hospital nurses remembered that, despite the excitement of getting the wage packet to see what the rise was, when they opened it the Hospital had deducted half a crown for board and lodgings - thus they weren't that much better off!

Student nurses' salary 1948
Year 1 £55 pa

Year 2 £65 pa

Year 3 £75 pa

Qualified nurses' salaries were £140 per year rising to £200 after 10 years' service, with four weeks holiday. Men and women were still paid different rates, and a staff nurse might earn £315 a year but a male nurse £325.

No money!
The NHS, although welcomed immediately, went into debt as people surged for free treatment. The Courier Yearbook of 1949 stated: *"Hospital costs have increased alarmingly during the year, and budget estimates have been exceeded by millions."* In fact locally the accounts of the Management Committee show that at the end of April 1949 the group was overspent by £19,452. The report states that this was due to salaries.

In 1950 the Minister wrote: *"The government is deeply concerned about the rapid increase in expenditure in relation to the national economy. The considered view of HM Government is that expenditure has now reached a level that must not be exceeded."*

The Committee, officially *'Number 12 Group Management Committee'*, tried to decide upon a new name. Several were proposed, including Kent & Sussex United Hospitals Group. The Sisters wrote to the Courier the week after complaining that they did not want to be part of a group that sounded like a football team!

The immediate priority was to amalgamate Pembury and Kent & Sussex Hospital into a District General Hospital Service for Tunbridge Wells. They proposed all obstetric and gynaecological services along with radiology and antenatal services to be handled by Pembury, whereas Kent & Sussex would deal with all acute medical and surgical work.

The Courier reacted angrily at the press being banned from Group Management Committee meetings. They cited the fact the Committee was spending huge sums of public money, and that the public had a right to know what was decided. Its headline screamed: *"Hospital Board decides to erect an anti-press iron curtain!"*

The Matron of the Maternity Home resigned, claiming lack of consultation by this 'remote' decision-making body, and the Courier reported that one of the reasons there might be lack of recruitment is that nurses might have to be interchangeable between Pembury and the Kent & Sussex. They said most regarded this thought with horror.

Another major change was the almost immediate establishment of an admissions office at Sherwood Park to control admissions to the hospitals. All GPs were reminded that all admissions now had to go through the admissions office prior to sending patients to hospital. A centralised finance department quickly followed, as did a new phenomenon: the waiting list.

In December 1948, the Minister wrote to all committees reminding them that in this day of the NHS there was no place for collecting to support hospitals. He specifically outlawed posters, collecting tins, flag days and fetes. He stated that the use of uniformed nurses to collect money must cease.

It was during the Bill reading that Bevan first said: *"I have always felt a shudder of repulsion when I have seen nurses and sisters who ought to be at their work, and students who ought to be at theirs, going about the streets collecting money for the hospitals."*

Pembury Estates Department. The red-door section housed the hospital's fire appliances until after the war

Nurse Training

The new Preliminary Training School for nurses that had opened at Blackhurst provided training for new entrants from both Pembury and Folkestone. Beryl Whiddett started her training there in 1947 and described her training. *"It was hard work and very much on- the-job training!"*

At the Kent & Sussex Hospital, a new teaching unit was opened in a vacant wartime hut, the old Ward 4, which Sister Gravelius transformed into a teaching facility. Next door, Ward 5 was turned into an occupational therapy ward.

Blackhurst was an old manor house, and staff were accommodated in rooms with six or seven beds, with the large downstairs rooms converted to classrooms. After three months students then moved to the hospital.

Pat Austin started her training at Blackhurst in 1952. She recalled: *"We were taught anatomy and physiology extensively – we had odd visits like having to visit the local sewage farm all in our uniforms, complete with hats and capes!"*

There was a lot of focus on diets and nutrition: *"You have to remember that rationing had only just ended and there was still poverty around. Often patients would need feeding up before surgery.*

"We didn't associate with the set above us and there was certainly no talking to the doctors. We worked 12-hour shifts with no time off for studying. Even after night duty we had to be ready for doctors' lectures at 11am. It was a very happy time, however. The wards were very regimented."

The wards had a strict regime. Pat Austin started on Medical Ward at the Kent & Sussex Hospital: *"As the most junior person there my role was clearly laid out: don't do anything involving patients unless told to do so! A lot of time was spent in the sluice, scrubbing bed pans!*

At quiet times we used to wash crepe bandages and re-roll them, making cotton wool balls or preparing gauze dressings – all of which was done on the ward. We always had convalescing patients on the ward who would help with ward tasks like the tea round or helping us with making dressings."

Stained glass in the Kent & Sussex Hospital Chapel

Beryl Whiddett recalled that Matron Fagelman ruled the hospital at Pembury:

"She carried out rounds which were very formal. She might suddenly pounce on you to provide a diagnosis or a patient's name - and heaven help you if you didn't know!"

The huts were difficult to heat with two coke burning boilers: *"The porters used to stoke them up and dust and ash would float everywhere! The wards were cleaned so that if there was even a speck of dust then there was trouble from Sister."*

Pat Austin remembered that at the Kent & Sussex: *"the cleaners on each ward were permanent and took pride in their ward and were supervised by the nursing staff. Everything was damp dusted in the morning.*

Every patient had a bath on admission to the hospital. Hygiene standards were low in a lot of households which didn't even have running water. It wasn't unusual for us to find patients were infested with fleas which quickly transferred to us. In fact we were warned in training about this. The only advice offered was to have a deep hot bath and completely immerse in it. Not always effective!"

Ambulance Services

Another problem that quickly became apparent was the abuse of ambulance services. The Minister reminded committees that using ambulances for long-distance transfers should be exceptional, and that trains would be cheaper. Ambulance services often used trains to transfer patients long distances and even to London for treatment. A compartment would be booked and a nurse would escort the patient. An ambulance would then meet the train at the other end. This was in an age when no hospital in England was more than six miles from a train station.

The ambulance service had been run by St John Ambulance and the Red Cross in Kent & East Sussex, as there was no state-run system. As part of the National Health Service, responsibility for providing an ambulance service was given to the Local Authorities. In the Tunbridge Wells area Kent County Council took over responsibility for running the ambulance service with a whole-time ambulance service, using St John Ambulance as agents to supplement it. But in East Sussex, St John Ambulance and Red Cross ran the service on an agency basis, which relied on St John Ambulance to provide the ambulance service until 1967.

A County Council Ambulance Station was opened at Pembury Hospital and remained there until 1951, before moving into Monson Road in Tunbridge Wells and later to Southborough in November 1961.

Late in 1949, the Regional Hospital Board restricted expenditure and stopped all recruitment to new posts and stopped all new services. Despite the cutbacks, however, the Management Committee were able to approve the increased order for ice cream to eight gallons a week at a cost of £3 15 shillings.

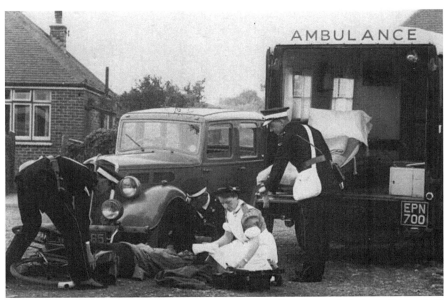

An East Sussex Ambulance Crew - 1949
Photo courtesy of Mr C.W. Hudson
131

*Pembury Hospital
Ambulance Crew, 1949*

The flu pandemic of 1951/2 saw all the hospitals completely full, and appeals went out for volunteers to come in and help.

In 1954, the new outpatients department opened having had its bomb damage repaired, although the advent of the NHS meant the original plans were slimmed down.

The Coronation of Queen Elizabeth II was a cause for celebration and the Management Committee approved two shillings per head for a celebration at each hospital, and funded a carnival float to go in the Tunbridge Wells Celebration Carnival on Coronation Day. Banners and bunting also decorated the hospital's sites. Many nurses remember a television was installed in the nurses' home for them to watch the coronation.

Nursing shortage

The nurse shortage during the post war era was acute. Mrs Spurrel, chair of the Hospital Management Committee Nursing Sub Committee, spoke on the subject at the Nurse Prize giving in 1953, reporting that: *"500 fewer beds are available across the group hospitals, as not enough nurses are available to meet demand."*

The staffing problem was becoming serious and the government urged committees to increase the amount of male nurses on the wards. They wrote that committees: *"should consider whether they might not profitably increase the number of male nurses employed, bearing in mind the longer average period of service obtainable from men than from women."*

The Courier reported in September 1948 that 300 beds were out of use at Pembury because of nursing shortages.

At the presentation of awards to newly qualified nurses in June 1951 at Pembury, Dame Barrie Lambert, a member of the HMC, spoke of the situation. She said: *"Already in the hospital service we are facing difficulty – just at a time when we are ready to go ahead our budget has been cut and cut and cut. All around there is a feeling of frustration."*

Mixing the Christmas puddings at Pembury in 1955

The reports from 1950 also indicate statistics on each hospital which showed wide variation in the use of beds. In 1949/50 the Kent & Sussex had 350 beds, but only 250 available. On average 212 beds per day were occupied. The cost per head of patient was one pound and sevenpence. The average cost at Pembury was one pound three shillings and a penny, with 628 beds but only 377 available. Kent & Sussex saw over 85,000 outpatients and Pembury 38,000.

The Minister became concerned with efficiency relating to bed capacity. He wrote that it was: *"keeping pace with demand but not reducing the waiting list. The reduction of the waiting list is a question of immediate priority. At all times an empty bed on a ward should be considered a proper matter for enquiry by responsible medical and nursing staff."*

Audrey Emerton, who nursed at the Kent & Sussex during the 1950s, said: *"The wards were very well run and efficient, all single-sex with Sisters who led by example. The hospital was very well run, too, with good teamwork."*

Statistics from Pembury in the first year of the NHS show us that Pembury had 628 beds but only half were usually full, as the average daily number of beds occupied was 306. The hospital had over 25,000 outpatient attendances in the first year of the NHS, reflecting the willingness of the public to take advantage of the new service. The hospital spent £1,403 on farms and gardens while managing an income of £2,533 against farms and gardens. The average cost per patient per week was fourteen pounds nine shillings and sixpence.

In 1952, the bread ovens at Pembury, which supplied fresh bread to the group hospitals and had been at Pembury since 1835, were closed. The Management Committee found them too uneconomical and so in May 1952 the ovens were closed.

At the Kent & Sussex Hospital, there were 350 beds and the average number of beds occupied daily was 250, leaving an average of available daily beds of 100. The hospital saw a remarkable total of 59,426 outpatient attendances in the first year. The average cost per patient per week was nine pounds and fourpence.

Last loaf of bread being baked at Pembury

TB and Polio

The cases of TB in England were increasing and The Times reported in early 1950 that over 400 patients a week were being killed by the disease. The need for more beds and nurses was highlighted. In 1951, the Courier exposed the appalling conditions at the Tunbridge Wells TB Clinic, where they still were using gas lighting and there was no hot water system. Asked why these conditions were not talked about a spokesman said: *"A certain section of Tunbridge Wells felt that TB was something that nice people didn't want to talk about."* Only three days after the headlines the local MP raised the matter in the House of Commons, and the clinic was quickly moved to the Homeopathic Hospital.

Polio and TB were major problems from the 1930s. Whilst TB began to decrease, especially as antibiotics became available, polio increased until adequate vaccines became available. Iron lungs kept those with paralysis alive. Mass vaccination campaigns were launched across Kent in 1957. Pat Austin, who trained at Kent & Sussex, recalled that tonsil operations were cancelled at the peak of outbreaks of polio due to the perceived risk to children.

In 1953 Pembury was designated a regional centre for polio cases, but protests from medical staff soon followed as there was no consultation with them. Extra equipment was provided by the Regional Board. Dr Grasby's daughter Janet recalled: *"There were many children in iron lungs, great metal boxes that enabled them to breathe. It was difficult for them to write and draw."*

Dr Grasby's wife Margaret taught them and kept them up to date with school work, as they were often in for weeks or months at a time.

Iron Lungs were a common sight

Statistics

The committee was soon questioning the reasons why costs were so different across the group, and why the average bed occupancy for the group was just 73%. This sort of discussion would continue, and still does today! Prescription charges were introduced in 1952: a flat rate 1/- charge with a flat rate £1 charge for dental work.

Nothing escaped the auditor's eye for economy in the hospitals, and Matrons were asked to ensure that floors were either polished less, or less polish was used. Visiting members were encouraged to check how polished the floors were.

By 1959, ten years later, bed numbers had reduced to 348 at Kent & Sussex and 590 at Pembury. The reports detail much more statistical analysis of the bed stock. Details were included on length of stay in hospital, how long beds stayed empty between patients, and the average number of patients treated per bed, along with costs. At Pembury over 230 beds were closed due to lack of staff.

The statistics generated by the new finance department identified that the costs per patient at Pembury were the highest in the group. These were quickly defended by the team at Pembury, who concluded that its uneconomical layout was bound to increase costs.

The drive to increase funding led to an increase in the cost of a private bed to £21 7s a week. The length of stay decreased to 16.8 days at Kent & Sussex.

Pembury Hospital 1949 from the Tonbridge Road

At Kent & Sussex, in 1958, surgical patients had a length of stay of 15 days. The reports show an increase in waiting lists brought in by the NHS in the 1950s. However, compared with today waiting lists were small - in 1959 the waiting list for orthopaedics was just 205. A comparison of the hospitals in 1959 compared with 1949 shows they treated 12.5% more patients, but showed an increase in the waiting list of 88%.

League of Friends

The League of Friends at Pembury was established by Dr Grasby, his wife Margaret, Miss Fagelman, the chaplain the Rev Stewart Browning, Miss Spurrel, Miss Thessiger and Miss Hughes, Headmistress of the Girls Grammar School. They carried on the tradition of the fetes and raised thousands for the hospital. The League of Friends continues to provide an important contribution to the life of the hospital.

New Matron

At Pembury, Matron Taubie Fagelman retired in 1957 having been Matron since 1940. Beryl Whiddett recalled: *"She was a disciplinarian but fair and always approachable. We got into great trouble after getting engaged without asking her permission. Married nurses couldn't work in those days, but we stayed on, becoming the first married nurses at Pembury!"*
Even then, they were only allowed to work in theatres and clinics with their wedding ring covered or removed. This continued until 1958, when more staff shortages meant a real push for married nurses.

Civil Defence became increasingly important during the 1950s, with the escalating tensions of the Cold War. The Government introduced the National Hospital Reserve Scheme to supplement the hospital service in a wartime or disaster scenario. Members of St John Ambulance and the Red Cross formed the backbone of the service along with trained nurses from the hospitals.

The Mobile First Aid Unit based at the Kent & Sussex Hospital competed in regional competitions, doing very well and always finishing in the top five. The ability to be ready was an essential wartime skill that carried over into peacetime.

Nancy Mewett joined the Kent & Sussex Hospital as a shorthand typist in February 1951, working for the Hospital Secretary and Matron.

"Staff had to sign a book in our office with the time of their arrival. At 0903 the hospital secretary would come to our office and draw a line across the book using red ink, so anyone arriving late would have to sign below it. There were no late arrivals in those days.

As rationing was still in progress all inpatients' ration books were brought to the clerk and kept in a filing cabinet. On discharge, the coupons were cut out or books marked to cover the patient's stay in hospital."

"The hospital always smelled and looked so clean, with the strong odour of disinfectant everywhere.

Consultants dictated letters for GPs after each clinic. They all went out by the evening post and arrived at GP surgeries the following morning."

Canteen Prices were increased in 1955 so that tea cost 3d a cup, coffee 4d a cup and an iced cake 4d.

In July 1949, open-ended visiting was approved on the children's wards at Pembury and the Kent & Sussex. Dr Norman Jacoby, along with Ward Sister Anne Bowley, increased the profile of this move which was not without its critics. Several national and regional talks were given by them promoting this modern approach, with parents even being able to stay on the ward. In his book Dr Jacoby recalled the idea was well received, but asking nurses to remove their hats was 'a step too far' for the nursing hierarchy!

Matron Joan Page recalled: *"Sister Bowley was a great character – the children always came first – and the ward at Pembury was always a happy place to be. I remember one Christmas I was doing my rounds and found her on the floor with no hat or apron, hastily wrapping presents for a new admission that had come in so they had presents to open! Each Christmas every child would receive a present, and the ward was decorated so beautifully."*

In 1956, an alternate surgical intake system was organised, so that Pembury and Kent & Sussex took surgical referrals on different days. This gave greater flexibility in the use of beds and helped with short-staffing problems on the wards.

August 1957 saw the retirement of Mr Burslem from the Hospital Management Committee. Over 200 people packed the hospital to mark the occasion. The next week the Courier headlines read 'Hospital Committee row feared' as the race to choose a successor caused uncertainty.

Christmas
Christmas was always a special time in the hospitals. Every ward would decorate with a different theme and the Matron and Chairman would choose a winner.

Pat Austin recalled: *"The consultants would always come in and carve turkey on the ward in a chef's hat. Each ward had a Christmas tree and Sister was given a small amount of money to buy a present for each patient from Father Christmas!"*

The most remembered event of Christmas at both Pembury and the Kent & Sussex Hospital was the carol singing around the wards. Pat Austin fondly recalled: *"We had our cloaks on the wrong way round so the red was showing and sang a carol on each ward. Everyone loved it. Often patients would have tears in their eyes. Even Matron would join us."*

Throughout the 1950s and 1960s the Christmas Revue was well attended: *"There were often outrageous skits on Consultants and Sisters. They were expected to laugh as we would all be straining to look at them!"*

Maternity

Although the Maternity Home in Calverley Park Gardens provided an excellent service, the Maternity Unit at Pembury also took on an increasingly important role. Dr Grasby, whose clinical specialism was obstetrics and gynaecology, had worked hard to increase the level of care at Pembury and turn it into a renowned centre of excellence. The Evening News in April 1952 carried an article on the new maternity methods employed at Pembury, written after significant investment in the Delivery and Postnatal wards, it described the Maternity Unit as a 'pioneer hospital.'

The long Victorian Nightingale Wards were converted into smaller wards and rooms, and mothers were encouraged to have their babies with them beside their beds rather than being taken to a nursery overnight: *"Modern babies are fed on demand whenever they are hungry!"*

The article went on to reveal the hospital's biggest change was towards expectant mothers: *"From the first visit when the young mother first meets her doctor she is put at ease – she goes on to join girls in the gym class in the physiotherapy department."*

It revealed that Pembury prided itself in the fact that new mothers went home after ten days post-delivery, wearing the clothes they had before they became pregnant. *"The warm, friendly atmosphere and absence of stern clinical air ... One felt here were perfectly normal, healthy women enjoying every minute of a most interesting experience. The department embraced new ideas - 'Some of the babies arrive under hypnosis, with no pain at all."*

Later, Pembury would pioneer the use of epidurals in labour and other new initiatives.

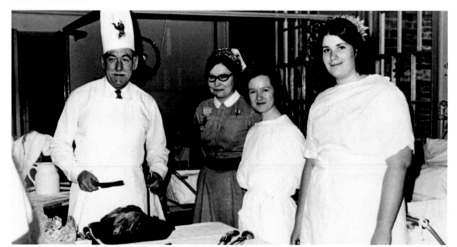

Christmas Day

Christmas Eve at Pembury, carol singing

Hospital horse

Pembury entrance 1949

The Camden and Abergavenny Tablet commemorating its handover to the NHS
Photo courtesy of The Tunbridge Wells Project

**Men and women
are needed <u>now</u> in**

**ASK AT YOUR LOCAL HEADQUARTERS OF
ST. JOHN AMBULANCE BRIGADE
OR THE BRITISH RED CROSS SOCIETY**

Chapter 7

1958 – 1970: Modernisation and a new hospital

In 1958, the NHS celebrated its tenth birthday. A decade of improvements in health and welfare were celebrated. The NHS had become firmly embedded in society and was part of daily life. Even after ten years of the NHS older residents were amazed at the benefits they enjoyed. Nurses recalled that older patients would say things like: *"I never thought I would be able to come to this hospital,"* reflecting on the fact that healthcare cost money and now it was free at the point of use.

1958 had started with the Asian Flu pandemic, which had already caused significant pressure on the NHS in the latter part of 1957. But just when the hospital thought the worst was over, another peak after Christmas meant the start of 1959 was extremely busy in the hospitals. The absence of nurses and other staff, along with the increase in admissions, caused significant pressure across the area.

The 44-hour week

After extensive campaigning, the nurses' working week was reduced to 44 hours. This led to an increase in nurse numbers but, with a national shortage of nurses, there was for the first time a real push for married nurses and part-time nurses to fill vacancies.

Miss Jane Jacobs, who had taken over from Miss Fagelman, was formerly Matron at the Maternity Home in Tunbridge Wells. She appealed for more part-time nurses to remain in the profession after marriage, realising it was the only way to rapidly increase the number of nurses on the wards. In 1960, she wrote an article for the Nursing Mirror on implementing the scheme at Pembury.

"There has had to be a certain amount of rearrangement of ward work so that the bulk of the work is done when staff are available. I know when I trained ... we had to have the baths done and the ward ready for rounds by 10am. Now, however, blanket baths have often to be done in the afternoons - and surely better that they should be done then rather than not at all."

She went on to write: *"I think the answer is to take the staff for the hours they can offer, and arrange work to fit in with them. Quite simply, we cannot run our hospitals without their assistance – we at Pembury still do not have enough staff."*

She concluded: *"We in the nursing profession are apt to resent change. It is so easy to say "When I trained we did this," but do not let us forget for one moment how tired we were in the old days, and how pleased we would have been to work a 44-hour week!"*

The following year she said: *"The general public has put us on a pedestal, not a comfortable seat. It is underpaid and overworked - but don't resent change."*

Change was certainly going to come – more quickly than it had ever done before.

Progress

Major advances in medicine were seen in the 1950s and 1960s. New ranges of antibiotics emerged, safe oral diuretics such as chlorothiazide in 1957 and frusemide appeared in 1965, propanalol soon followed for angina and blood pressure. Aerosols for the treatment of asthma were introduced in 1960.

Steadily, the amount of time patients spent in hospital was decreasing. Beryl Whiddett, working at Pembury, recalled:

"Things changed beyond all recognition after the widespread introduction of antibiotics. Initially, they had to be given every four hours, day and night, but gradually they became less frequent and oral administration greatly improved things further. We used to sterilise everything on the wards but, gradually, more disposables were introduced and a sterilising department carried out autoclaving."

The new Radiotherapy Unit was opened at Pembury in August 1963 by the Marchioness of Abergavenny. This unit replaced the Guy's Unit that had to be closed. Dr John Carter-Braine came from Guy's in 1939 and installed his own kit in Sherwood Park, before it moved to Pembury while Guy's was rebuilt following bombing. This meant that, once again, Pembury was able to offer specialist cancer treatments only available in a few hospitals outside London.

In 1960 The Management Committee debated how to remember Alderman R.H. Burslem, who had died that year.

His long and distinguished service to the hospitals in Tunbridge Wells was well known and appreciated. He was Chairman of both the Kent & Sussex Hospital Committee and the Tunbridge Wells Hospital Management Committee. He also served as a member of the Regional Hospital Board, and as Mayor of Tunbridge Wells between 1933 and 1935. He was passionate about staff welfare and worked hard on getting the best nurses' accommodation for staff.

The committee concluded that the nurses' home at the Kent & Sussex Hospital should be called Burslem House as a tribute, with the Alderman's portrait on prominent display.

Miss Kendall, Assistant Matron, and Sister Grey, Home Sister, on Ward 11a at Christmas

The Cold War was intensifying and the Civil Defence and National Hospital Reserve was on high alert. A large-scale exercise was organised in May 1961 to test major emergency and Civil Defence arrangements. The Kent & Sussex Hospital played a very active part in the National Hospital Reserve Scheme, winning competitions and using members on wards to help in staffing shortages.

Further moves were made to centralise services, and from April 1960 all gynaecology was centralised at Pembury Hospital. Although the Maternity Home carried out most straightforward deliveries, an increasing number of births were occurring at Pembury. It was a constant aim of the Management Committee to secure one united District General Hospital Service for Tunbridge Wells. However, the two hospitals were very separate and resistant to losing their distinct identities.

In 1961, Hospital Radio Tunbridge Wells started, providing a limited service at the Kent & Sussex Hospital. It merged with Pembury in 1971, supported by the League of Friends. This service expanded to cover most of the Tunbridge Wells Hospitals by the early 1970s.

Man from the Ministry
During 1961, a new day hospital facility, including Occupational Therapy, was opened on the Pembury site. The new unit was formally opened by the Chief Medical Officer at the Ministry of Health, Dr Godber, on August 3rd 1961.

Enoch Powell, the Health Minister, visited the Kent & Sussex Hospital on March 22nd 1961. Later that year he gave approval for the contraceptive pill to be available on the NHS, one of the defining moments of the service. Later, he announced The Hospital Plan for England, which set the direction for travel for England. The Plan set out the need for District General Hospitals with between 600 and 800 beds, normally serving a population of 100,000 to 150,000 people, with all facilities under one roof.

This had always been an aim of the Hospital Management Committee: all they needed was the money to build one. Assistant Matron Joan Page, who went around with him, said: *"It was clear he felt Tunbridge Wells needed a new hospital, and we all believed that the hospital plan might give us the opportunity to get a new building."*

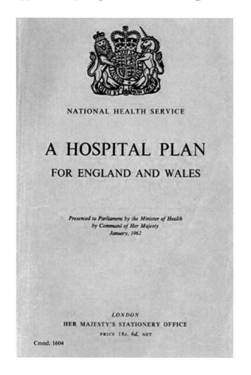

NATIONAL HEALTH SERVICE

A HOSPITAL PLAN

FOR ENGLAND AND WALES

Presented to Parliament by the Minister of Health
by Command of Her Majesty
January, 1962

LONDON
HER MAJESTY'S STATIONERY OFFICE
PRICE 18s. 6d. NET

Cmnd. 1604

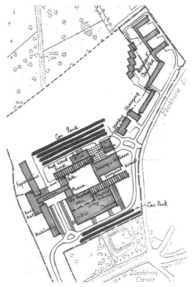

A plan of the proposed new hospital at Sherwood Park 1963

A new hospital

The subject of a new single-site District General Hospital became a hot topic during the early 1960s, with project groups looking at several options.
The most favoured option considered by the Regional Hospital Board in 1963 was to build a new 700-bed District Hospital on the Sherwood Park Site, on the Pembury Road in Tunbridge Wells. The proposal included a helipad and accommodation for staff. The Regional Board reminded the Management Committee that this was a long-term plan and indeed, despite agreeing the principle, found greater needs elsewhere in the South East.

The Kent & Sussex Hospital continued to expand, with various huts and changes to the fabric including conversion of the main theatre into a Honeywell twin-theatre design with up-to-date ventilation systems. This revolutionary modular system updated theatres in old hospitals up and down the country, by using prefabricated materials and standard design that were simply built into a space. It featured foot-operated doors and standardised controls into a hexagonal design. In her first report the new Matron said:

"The hospital is really bursting at the seams, just like a child in outgrown clothes, and we haven't nearly enough space for all our needs.

How often, when some of us waste time travelling between the hospitals, do we wish that the District Hospital we hoped to plan this year were not just a dream? How much more efficient could we be if we were working on one site?"

This comment would be echoed by staff at the hospitals for the next 40 years.

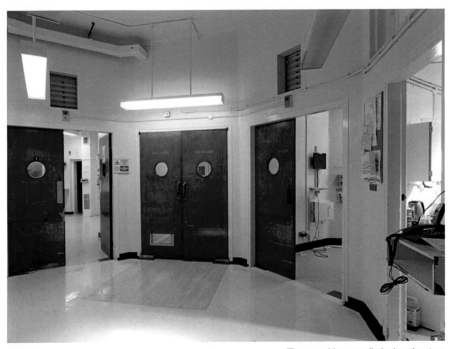

The new Honeywell-design theatres

In 1962, the Courier ran a major story on the work of the Kent & Sussex Hospital to raise the profile of the NHS locally, revealing it cost £7,000 a week to run, with six tonnes of coal a day being used to keep the boilers going, and 18 laundry staff laundering over 14,000 pieces a week.

Emergency lighting was considered at Pembury in 1962, but the Management Committee was content that the candles already issued to each ward were sufficient.

A major report into the dangers of smoking was published by the Royal College of Physicians in 1962, in which they pointed out the health effects. The Management Committee banned the sale of cigarettes in public areas of the hospitals and introduced new smoking rules. However, following complaints from junior doctors, cigarette vending machines were allowed in the Doctors' Mess. This arrangement continued even after the banning of cigarette advertising on TV in 1965. In 1962 70% of men and 40% of women smoked, and complications from smoking were beginning to find their way into hospitals.

Accident and Emergency

The advent of faster roads and faster cars brought a new pattern of serious injury into hospitals. The whole subject of managing accidents and emergencies was discussed nationally. It was widely recommended that more accident centres, providing 24-hour enhanced care, and fewer casualty departments was the way forward.

The question of casualty departments was brought into focus in 1961 when a capital bid for a new department at Pembury was refused, mainly because of an impending new hospital. The unit at Pembury had only three cubicles, and a report confirmed that seriously injured patients were often waiting and being treated in corridors. Attendances had increased from 1556 in 1951 to 3339 in 1960. A working party concluded that a purpose-built accident centre should be built at the Kent & Sussex Hospital, to take all accident and emergency admissions from the group in one specialised centre. However the cost of building the centre was so high that the work was deferred.

Accident centres were built at Canterbury, Medway and Ashford, and the MP for Maidstone raised with the Minister in the House of Commons in 1967 his concerns that in West Kent the Hospital Plan had stalled, with no sign of a new hospital being built. The A&E department had a VIP patient in 1965 when a Government Minister was admitted after a horse riding accident.

An alternate casualty and orthopaedic intake system was set up from 1960, so that the casualty departments accepted admissions on different days of the week. The system continued until 1985, when the new Culverden Wing opened.

Audrey Emerton was a Casualty Staff Nurse in the 1950s at the Kent & Sussex Hospital. She recalled there were no specialist A&E staff, with Outpatients Nurses running Casualty. She described it as one of the *"most valuable years"* of her career. The Casualty Departments saw only the accidents and emergencies that came in, with nearly all GP referrals going direct to a bed on a ward.

Serious road traffic accidents like this one on the A20 in 1962 were increasing, as was the seriousness of the injuries. Helmets were seldom worn and seatbelts hadn't been introduced

Intensive Care

Research from Canada suggested that improved survival could be made if seriously ill patients were cohorted into single areas with monitors and specially-trained nursing staff. The concept of intensive care was born, although it would be the vision of Dr Ronnie King that would see the first Intensive Care Unit opened at Kent & Sussex Hospital in 1970, in what was Ward 15 on the top floor. Dr Mike Everest was appointed Consultant Physician to the two hospitals in 1969, and described the unit as

"a happy and successful unit with a very high standard of nursing."

The concept of intensive care was still not universally accepted, however, and Dr King had to battle with some old-school consultant colleagues who felt that it was not necessary. Dr Everest recalled:

"Some colleagues were openly hostile to the idea, especially some of the surgeons."

A further report criticised the Outpatients Department at Pembury, whose attendances had increased from 6,980 in 1949 to 8,138 in 1960. The report observed that patients were frequently standing outside waiting in the rain.

The changing nurse

The early 1960s saw many different views on nursing practice, including the introduction of Enrolled Nurses and a move to more academic training. Muriel Powell, Matron of St George's Hospital, chaired the Standing Nursing Advisory Committee and challenged the old ethos of waking patients early, noise from staff and some task- orientated procedures, arguing that patient-centred care was better.

The way that wards were run became a topic for review, with the publication of reports including 'The Pattern of the inpatients Day', which the Hospital Management Committee implemented in Tunbridge Wells.

It recognised that with an increasing number of day cases, better and quicker recovery and more seriously ill patients being cohorted into intensive care areas, the wards were becoming different.

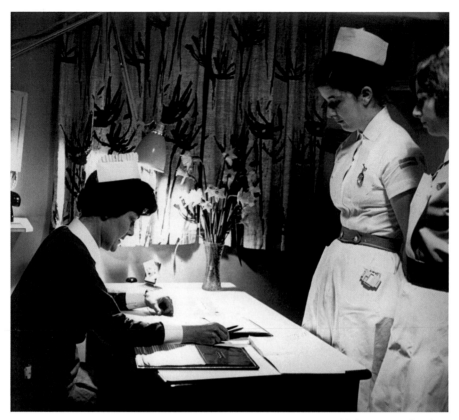

Night report at Pembury

Audrey Emerton, who nursed at the Kent & Sussex Hospital, became a Ward Sister on the ENT Ward. She recalled that at the Kent & Sussex, wards had already become more patient-centred than most, and a lot of the recommendations in the report had already been implemented by Matron Frere.

It was with this in mind that the 1966 Salmon Report was established into nursing management. Chaired by Dr Brian Salmon, it proposed an entirely new system of nurse administration. It aimed to put nurses at the heart of decision-making, at an equal level with Group Secretaries and medical staff.

During 1968, the so called Salmon concept of nursing management reform was the big talked-about subject in hospitals.

He had planned to phase this in gradually over several years. However, the Government had decided that it was to be brought in more rapidly, with pay rises for nurses. The other effect was to be the abolition of matrons, who would be replaced by a Chief Nursing Officer at each management committee table and grades of nursing officer in each area of expertise. Ward sisters would be freed to nurse and manage their wards.

The Salmon working group first visited Tunbridge Wells in March 1969, following a Management Committee resolution in December 1968 to *"do everything possible to adopt Salmon early."* An advert, which went out nationally, was placed for a Chief Nursing Officer. Audrey Emerton was the successful candidate, having been at the Teaching Unit at Bromley.

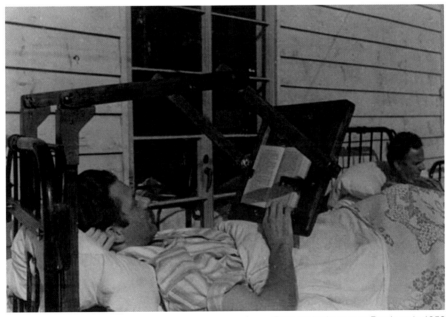

Patients in the sun at Pembury in 1958

The seeds of change were also sown in 1960 when Enoch Powell and his team considered that having three separate funding streams for the NHS, for Hospitals, GPs and Local Health, was a great weakness. A reorganisation of the NHS was inevitable.

Change was in the air again!

Summing the changes up Matron wrote in her report to the Tunbridge Wells Nurses League in 1968:

"Some are naturally resistant to change, fearing the unknown. We must appreciate however that the organisation which does not change will die. As nurses we must stop looking over our shoulder to Florence Nightingale and forward to the needs of our patients in the 1970s and 1980s."

Dr Brian Hosford (1904 - 1989)

Dr Hosford was born in 1904, the son of a London GP and qualified at St Bartholomew's Hospital London in 1926. After working at Great Ormond Street he moved to Tunbridge Wells joining a GP practice, and was given an honorary consultancy at the Kent & Sussex as Cardiologist and Physician.

He was a member of the Territorial Army and, at the outbreak of war, was called up to serve. After Dunkirk, he was taken prisoner of war at Le Touquet Field Hospital.

He remained a prisoner of war until 1944, when he was liberated by the Americans and returned to the Kent & Sussex Hospital. He became a Consultant Physician when the NHS was created, and eventually retired in 1969. He died in the hospital he loved, aged 85, in 1989.

He was admired by all for his contribution to the development of the Kent & Sussex Hospital.

His replacement, Dr Mike Everest, recalled he was 'universally respected.'

End of an era

Retirement of Matron Frere

In 1962, Matron Frere retired, and was given a fine send-off. All the consultants spoke highly of her at her retirement party, and there was great sadness at her departure. She was invited to a Queen's Garden Party at Buckingham Palace in recognition of her hard work.

At the retirement party, she said: *"It is thanks to the loyalty and help from you all – no Matron could achieve anything without this. I stand here a very proud person. You and this fine hospital will always be in my prayers. You know I have always made my own morning cup of tea and washed my cup up!"*

David Nicholson, who was a hospital administrator, recalled being trained to go and see her by one of the assistant matrons: *"Matron sat in a high chair and looked down at you. I had to remember never to turn my back on her. The first time I went into see her I was so focused on not turning my back on her I tripped over the doorstop on the way out!"*

Anne Preece, who nursed at the Kent & Sussex in 1957, said: *"She was a strong-willed but gracious lady who knew everyone's name. She had complete control. Her rounds meant everything being shipshape and spotless. Whoever was in charge had to meet her and take her around, introducing her to each patient and giving a diagnosis."*

Matron Frere had seen the hospital through its inception, through the war years, and into the NHS. Audrey Emerton, who worked with her. said: *"She was a petite lady, very precise and with very high standards. She stood her ground with administrators and consultants alike. She was very fair but ruled with a rod of iron. Her flat was in the hospital and it was not unknown for her to carry out night rounds of the wards."*

Miss Joan Page started her career in the East End during the Second World War at the Queen's Hospital for Children as a sick children's nurse, before completing her general training at Guy's Hospital. Her first post as a ward sister was at the Royal Free Hospital in 1949, where she later became Night Superintendent.

While at the Royal Free she spent six months studying at a hospital near Copenhagen before returning as Home Sister at Guy's Hospital. After a secondment to the King's Fund during which she spent three months at the Kent & Sussex Hospital, she returned to Guy's as Assistant Matron. In April 1959 she took up the Assistant Matron post at Kent & Sussex Hospital.

Matron Frere standing next to new Matron Joan Page at her retirement presentation 1962

When Miss Jacobs moved from Pembury to the Department of Health as a nursing officer at the end of 1963, the question of nursing leadership was raised. It was decided that, to promote integration, there would be one matron covering the two hospitals. Miss Page took over as Matron of the two hospitals in 1964, with Margaret Pilbeam as Assistant Matron.

A General Nursing Council inspection the previous year had insisted that there could not be two schools of nursing in Tunbridge Wells, so amalgamation of the Pembury and Kent & Sussex Schools was critical to continued nurse training in the area. In April 1964 a new Tunbridge Wells School of Nursing was announced, with increasingly more training provided on the Pembury Site. The two hospitals had two very separate identities and histories, and further integration was a difficult process.

Miss Page recalled:

"I knew getting the sisters behind me was key, and we set out to get Kent & Sussex sisters and Pembury sisters to meet each other and swap ideas and thoughts. This was important as each school and each hospital had developed its own nursing practice. It was important that the students from the newly-merged school learned one way of doing things – the Tunbridge Wells way. Working as a team with my deputy Margaret Pilbeam, it was a rewarding time. The two hospitals had such a happy atmosphere."

TUNBRIDGE WELLS GROUP HOSPITAL MANAGEMENT COMMITTEE

Visit of

Her Royal Highness The Duchess of Kent

to the

Kent and Sussex Hospital and Pembury Hospital

on

Thursday, 20th March, 1969

CARD OF ADMISSION

Matron Frere with the Hospital Secretary Don Raynor in 1960

Dr Fowler and Sister Pryer on Ward 11 at Christmas 1960

Matron Jane Jacobs

DrJacoby, Dr Leedham and Dr Gilford at the opening of the Medical Library at Pembury

Nursing shortage

The nursing staffing situation became dire again in 1962, with over 150 beds closed because of lack of nurses. Miss Jacobs, Matron at Pembury, held an emergency meeting to consider cutting back on surgery as she only had 52 nurses instead of 120. Matron Page recalled: *"The nursing shortage was a national problem. Once I recall I had only 14 nurses for the whole of Pembury Hospital on one particular night shift."*

A nurse recruitment officer was appointed in 1965 to try to find new nurses, as the 84-hour fortnight forced the need for even more nurses when it came in on 1st February 1965.

The Ministry of Health had been recruiting in former colonies since the inception of the NHS, and by 1955 there were recruitment programmes in 15 colonies or former colonies. By the end of 1965 over 5,000 nurses from Jamaica alone were in the NHS. Commonwealth nurses were now training at Tunbridge Wells and, in 1966, the Gold Medal was awarded to Euphrema Dillion from Trinidad and Tobago. The matrons praised the work that Commonwealth nurses were doing at Tunbridge Wells.

In the training school report in 1963, it was reported that nurses from twelve countries were training at Tunbridge Wells. Later, in 1968, Matron wrote: *"While students of other disciplines riot and protest, ours have learnt to live happily in a multi-racial community taking pride in serving anyone in need."*

Miss Jacobs sadly died in January 1965 while working at the Department of Health, and the Management Committee stood in tribute to her at their next meeting. In the Courier she was described as:

"a trim, brisk, perhaps slightly formidable woman, with passionate enthusiasm and pride - an inspiration to everyone." Another nurse recalled: "In days of staffing shortages she could be seen trudging up the stairs with buckets of soiled nappies from the nursery – she was never starchy."

When the new theatre on the Children's Ward was opened it was called the Jane Jacobs Theatre in her memory.

Progress

The Isolation Hospitals had become steadily unused for their original purpose, and in 1966 the Tunbridge Wells Isolation Hospital was closed and renamed Hawkenbury Hospital. This was reopened in June 1966 as a hospital catering for geriatric patients.

Severe floods hit Tonbridge in autumn 1968, causing damage to hundreds of homes. The Council turned to Pembury Hospital to help with the drying out of people's belongings in the laundry and boiler house. Staff worked free of charge to help.

Tetanus infection was found in Pembury theatres due to inadequate ventilation systems.

Matron made reference to progress in her report to the School of Nursing prize-giving in 1968. She said: *"We realise the nurse of tomorrow will have to accept unprecedented responsibilities, and with new situations and demands in a rapidly changing society, her education must prepare her to meet these without undue strain.*

I am very conscious that new techniques, such as those for cases of cardiac arrest, impose responsibilities on young shoulders which they cannot carry alone. In the past year a number of patients' lives have been saved through the prompt action of nurses who have sent out the 'Mayday' signal, to which all available medical staff respond immediately."

New treatments for cardiac arrest appeared in the early 1960s, with mouth-to-mouth respiration and chest compressions as the advocated treatments. External defibrillation with electric shocks became widespread, although there was only one machine per hospital to start with. The machines were heavy and not very mobile, and had to be taken to the appropriate ward by porters.

The advent of a measles vaccine in 1966 brought relief from the common childhood infection, and by 1967 routine vaccination of children was being recommended. This resulted in a reduction in infections and admissions to children's wards. Earlier, in 1962, vaccination against polio was introduced, leading to a significant decrease in cases.

Advances in medicine continued and in 1968 the first heart transplant was carried out. The second was carried out on a gentleman from Pembury, who had been taken to Pembury Hospital and then transferred to London. Tragically, he died a few days later - but it set the scene for a growing and life-saving sphere of medicine.

In 1968 the National Hospital Reserve Scheme was brought to an end by the Government, but locally the scheme was continued as a way of attracting more staff.

Sister Gravelius, the Sister Tutor who had devoted a large part of her life to student nurses at Kent & Sussex, retired in 1968 and was replaced by Sister Thelma Dillistone. Having trained at St Bartholomew's Hospital in London she was a friend of Matron Frere. Many nurses have spoken of their fond memories of her devotion to teaching high standards of practical nursing care at the hospital.

Sister Gravelius was asked to represent the UK at the Red Cross International Conference in Geneva in 1962. She was also commended for her work in writing nursing textbooks for St John Ambulance and the British Red Cross.

In 1965, she gave a speech to student nurses recognising the need for change: *"I think we all realise that if nurse training in this country is to maintain its reputation for producing the most efficient bedside nurse in the world, we must seriously look to our methods of training and be prepared to alter them to meet modern standards of surgery and medicine."*

Audrey Emerton, who worked with her at the Kent & Sussex Hospital, said: *"She was quite a frightening person to look at, but underneath she had a soft side. She expected very high standards and got results which produced very good nurses.'* Anne Preece said: *'She was a formidable lady, but very supportive. She was good at lecturing, and nurses had the highest respect for her."*

Margaret Barnden started her training at Kent & Sussex Hospital in January 1968: *"We started at the K&S then did our second year at Pembury, before returning to K&S for the final year. It was really a home from home. We had a home sister who was very motherly and looked after us and helped us with problems. Breakfast was always laid out for us!"*

Recalling Sister Dillistone she said: *"She was very dignified and professional. She had very high standards, but was very fair."*

Royal visits

The League of Friends at Pembury completed a new building for patients' relatives in 1965, along with other improvements, and in July HRH Princess Marina, Dowager Duchess of Kent, visited to open the building and tour the site.

In March 1969, the Duchess of Kent visited both Pembury and Kent & Sussex Hospitals, to meet the staff and open an extension to the Ophthalmology Unit at Kent & Sussex and the new Delivery Suite at Pembury.

Don Rayner, Hospital Secretary at the Kent & Sussex Hospital, was invited as a guest at the Queen's Garden Party.

End of an era again

At Pembury, Dr Grasby retired after long service to the hospital in June 1968.

At his farewell he paid tribute to the friendly staff at Pembury. His long career and reputation as the 'father of Pembury Hospital' was praised by all who attended. In particular, tributes were paid to his wartime service. In his retirement letter he recalled that the hospital was once completely self-sufficient, with its own tailor, bakehouse, and a department of engineers who could make instruments for the theatres.

His long association with Pembury Hospital, in changing it from a workhouse infirmary to a modern hospital, along with his management of Pembury in the war, will not be quickly forgotten.

Another retirement in 1970 was that of Kitty Macintosh, the Chief Pharmacist who had given long service to the Kent & Sussex Hospital from 1936. She was a branch officer of Tunbridge Wells Red Cross and was affectionately known as 'Kitty Mac' by staff. Joan Page recalled: *"She was a marvellous person and ran the pharmacy like clockwork – somehow she always managed to get a drug even if it was in short supply. It was not unusual for someone to be dispatched to the station to pick up a drug sent down by train from a London hospital."*

Dr E D Y Grasby

Disasters

On 5th Nov 1967, the Hither Green train crash occurred, which involved a Hastings to Charing Cross Train via Tunbridge Wells. Forty were killed and over 80 injured. Amongst the dead was a student nurse from Kent & Sussex and Pembury Hospitals. Juliet McPherson-Heard was working on the Children's Ward at Pembury and was a well liked and popular student nurse. Matron reported at the School prize-giving: *"She was only twenty but during the two years we had known her she lived life to the full and was a happy girl."*

On the evening of 4th January 1969, a railway accident occurred between Paddock Wood and Marden involving three trains in thick fog. A total of 18 ambulances from all over Kent attended, and a mobile medical team from Pembury Hospital attended the scene.

The team worked in difficult conditions with emergency services to deal with casualties, who were then taken to the West Kent Hospital in Maidstone. Visibility was down to 25 yards, with thick mud along side the wreckage. Four people died in the accident.

The two hospitals cleared 120 beds. The Sunday Express headline read: *"Nurses refuse time off owed for big crash alert."* The editorial went on to say:

"For those hours of purely voluntary toil they were entitled to receive time off. There was not one who claimed it. No amount of money can buy such dedicated selfless service. And yet we still quibble about nurses pay."

An aircraft crash near Gatwick on 5th January 1969, that killed 50 people and injured 15, caused major accident plans to be activated by the Group, as casualties were taken to Queen Victoria Hospital with the Kent & Sussex on standby.

At a meeting afterwards between Matron and the main consultants at Pembury, it was agreed to review major incident arrangements. The team had to be taken by hospital coach to the incident site - although the driver lost his way in the dark and there was no formal protective clothing for the team. A working party made improvements that were tested.

Black spot

Until the construction of the Pembury Bypass in 1987, the roads outside Pembury were notorious for road accidents, as a 70 mph speed limit was in force and all the traffic on the main A21 had to pass the hospital entrance. Accidents were common and improvements had been called for since the early 1950s.

In May 1969, however, things came to a head as a visitor who had got off a bus outside the hospital was killed by a lorry. Immediate improvements were ordered with a bus lay-by and traffic islands constructed. The speed limit was reduced. However, many motorists complained that the improvements were just as dangerous.

Margret Barnden recalled: *"The A21 was always a nightmare until the new bypass was built in the 1980s. At weekends, especially in the summer, it was often one long traffic jam, with traffic on its way to the coast or returning in the evening."*

The end of the Swinging Sixties

The end of the 1960s saw an economic crisis, which meant the government had to reduce public expenditure. The government felt the only real alternative to reducing the hospital building programme was to reimpose prescription charges. A charge of 2/6 per item was introduced.

Emmanuel Church next to the hospital was closed in 1969, due to falling congregations, and purchased by the Hospital Management Committee.

On New Year's Eve 1969, the Courier reported on its front page: 'Doctors criticise Hospital Theatres', while nationally the People newspaper reported: 'Danger at the Hospital'. The publicity surrounded the release of a report by hospital consultants on the state of the operating theatres at Pembury Hospital. The report condemned both theatres as inadequate and dangerous. There was no recovery room, no storage, no rest or changing rooms and no sluice. They complained that in the summer, temperatures were too high, with air conditioning or cooling needed. This was to be top of Pembury's list of improvements for the start of the 1970s.

We end this chapter as we started, with an influenza outbreak. Christmas 1969 saw the start of another epidemic. The Courier reported 70 nurses off sick. Only emergencies were being admitted and outpatients appointments were cancelled. Volunteers were drafted in to assist on the wards.

The Swinging Sixties were coming to an end and the approaching new decade was starting on a note of economic uncertainty. Change both politically and socially was in the air, and the NHS would not escape. What would the 1970s hold for the hospitals?

Kent & Sussex Hospital Kitchens

Car Park Construction at Pembury

Tunbridge Wells carnival float by the School of Nursing

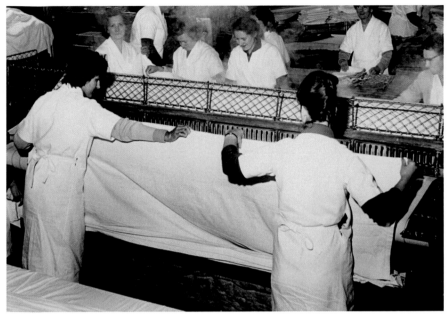

Laundry at Kent & Sussex Hospital

The Porters' Van

The covered way to the nurses' home was a central design feature of the Kent & Sussex Hospital. However, it had to be dissected when the main road was opened up, to enable the Culverden Wing to be used

The long hard winter in 1963. Snow fell Christmas 1962 and was on the ground until March 1963

Chapter 8

1970 - 1982 All change! A new hospital?

As the new decade started change was in the air right across the NHS, but with the Hong Kong Flu epidemic causing major difficulties and industrial and political unrest rife it was a bleak outlook.

The Hospital Management Committee announced an overspend of £20,000 at the end of the 1970/71 financial year, and the Regional Hospital Board announced that a new hospital was unlikely for at least 20 years. The new year brought with it a new decade and a great deal of change that would affect every level of the NHS.

Matron Joan Page retired in March 1970, after amalgamating the two hospitals' nursing structure and bringing together the School of Nursing. The hospitals, however, retained their very distinct identities.

The Salmon nursing structure was fully introduced during 1970 and was not immediately popular. Some consultants argued that experienced staff were being promoted away from the ward, while others argued that having a senior nurse at the boardroom table put nursing where it should be: at the heart of decision making.

Audrey Emerton was appointed the group's Chief Nursing Officer in April 1970. This was the most senior nursing post created at Tunbridge Wells. She was previously Casualty Sister, Night Sister then Ward Sister on Ward 12, before going to St George's Hospital and later heading up the teaching unit at Bromley.

Margaret Barnden, who had trained at Kent & Sussex, qualified as Salmon was being introduced and recalled that 'some Ward Sisters moved into Nursing Officer roles and Junior Sister posts began to be commonplace. Some people began to feel left out if they were 'just' a Staff Nurse.'

Baroness Audrey Emerton

Audrey Emerton attended Tunbridge Wells Girls Grammar School and was a Cadet with Tunbridge Wells St John Ambulance. She trained as a nurse at St George's Hospital London gaining State Registration in 1956, joining as a Staff Nurse at the Kent & Sussex and later Night and Ward Sister. In 1968 she became Principal Tutor at Bromley and returned as Chief Nursing Officer to Tunbridge Wells. In 1974 she was appointed Regional Nursing Officer to South East Thames Regional Health Authority. She was chair of the UKCC and was a previous Commissioner for Kent St John Ambulance and later Chief Commander. She was made a Dame in 1989 and created Baroness Emerton of Tunbridge Wells and Clerkenwell in 1997. She was previously Chairman of Brighton Healthcare NHS Trust and was renowned for her work in closing down large asylums such as Darenth Park in the 1980s.

Industrial unrest

Industrial unrest and the national economic crisis of the early 1970s saw a three-day week, power cuts and strikes affecting the country. An increasingly militant atmosphere appeared. Nationally, nurses and other NHS workers were fighting for more pay and a shorter working week.

At the end of January 1970, the COHSE Union organised a protest march through Tunbridge Wells to the Assembly Hall. However, even though nationally, health workers were involved in large demonstrations the Tunbridge Wells protest attracted just 10 marchers. The Assembly Hall meeting that could have held 1,000 just attracted 50. The Courier headlined: 'Nurses protest march dies on its feet!'

The deteriorating national economic picture towards the end of 1970 saw power cuts across the country, affecting even hospitals. Newspapers reported that an operation at the Homeopathic had to be completed by torchlight, and even those hospitals with generators, such as Pembury and the Kent & Sussex, had power only for essential services at times.

The new Intensive Care Unit at the Kent & Sussex Hospital was becoming a well used resource, and in its first 11 months 390 patients were admitted. One of the first patients described it as: *"something from Dr Who's space ship!"*

Pembury Hospital made the national news again in April 1970 when babies were given bottles of feed that had been made up with salt instead of sugar. The Sun claimed: *"Tots won't take a tot with a pinch of salt!"* An inquiry found no one to blame for the mix-up.

The children's ward received a visit from Sooty and Sweep together with Harry Corbett in January 1971, in celebration of Sweep's 21st birthday.

Leybourne Grange
In 1971, Leybourne Grange HMC was amalgamated with Tunbridge Wells and a front page news item in the Sunday People newspaper on the treatment of patients set off an inquiry by the Regional Hospital Board. The paper screamed: 'The bullies in our hospitals!'

Allegations surrounded assaults by staff and maltreatment of long-term patients. This was one of many inquiries into long-term institutions across England, revealing a hidden world in many of ill-treatment and low standards.

Audrey Emerton, as Chief Nursing Officer, spent much of her time trying to modernise care, and later in her career was to be instrumental in closing long-term institutions at Darenth Park and Leybourne. She recalled her first visit to Leybourne, saying simply: *"I had never seen anything quite like it."*

John Simons, one of the original consultants who came across to the Kent & Sussex Hospital from the old General Hospital, died in February 1971. He had trained at Guy's Hospital and, although invalided out of the Army in the First World War, spent six years in the Sudan. Staff recalled he was often called the father of the Kent & Sussex Hospital.

Theatre crisis at Pembury
Following protests by medical staff about theatres, the Regional Hospital Board announced capital funding of a new twin-theatre complex to be built in front of the maternity block. It would be *"one of the most modern theatres in the county"* with air conditioning, a recovery room and a Theatre Sterile Supply Department below, connected by lifts to the theatres.

The consultants had been working in the original theatres. Dr Loveday, a Consultant Anaesthetist, recalled that the theatres were divided by a public corridor which surgeons and instruments often had to cross. They could not have been cleaned properly. One of the theatres had a glass roof and created greenhouse conditions. There was no recovery room and no proper anaesthetic room.

The new theatres cost £250,000 and were opened by Sir Henry d'Aviigdor Goldsmid, the local MP, in July 1973.

Hospital's theatre danger to patients, says doctors' report

Opening of the new Pembury Theatres: Dr Loveday, Consultant Anaesthetist; Neville Gibson, Consultant Surgeon; Mrs Lodh, Nursing Officer; Mrs. J Cockrill, Chair of the Hospital Management Committee; Sir Henry d'Avigdor Goldsmid MP

Change in the air

In February 1972, the former Rosemont Hotel in Tunbridge Wells was bought to provide accommodation for doctors.

Later in 1972, the laundry at the Kent & Sussex Hospital was closed and all work transferred to Pembury in a central linen exchange. Later in 1976 the laundry services were transferred to Eastbourne to save money, and the laundry at Pembury closed.

In 1970, Dr Robin Loveday was appointed as a Consultant Anaesthetist at Pembury, with an interest in Obstetrics. He introduced epidural anaesthesia to Tunbridge Wells, making Pembury one of the first units to use this technique. He recalled:

"There was a degree of opposition to start with, as with any change, but soon Pembury became a pioneering unit."

March 1973 saw the opening of the new Postgraduate Medical Centre at the Kent & Sussex by Lord Aberdare, Minister of State at the Department of Health and Social Security.

The project saw the Regional Board, local residents and the Management Committee raise funds for the new centre. It provided modern teaching facilities for the medical staff costing £70,000, of which £26,000 was raised locally. The idea was one of Dr Ronnie King's; he spearheaded an appeal with local businesses and GPs as well as colleagues. Appeals included 'Buy a Brick' and 'Name a chair', along with appeals to charities and staff.

Dr Mike Everest said:

"The contribution made by Ronnie King was outstanding, in terms of teaching, education and his vision of the future in areas such as Intensive Care. He was a great committee man, able to get things done to improve things for staff and patients alike. He was a big influence with a tremendous character."

Opening of the Postgraduate Centre - Dr King far right

The new library facilities

The new library replaced the old ones, a medical library opened in 1965 and a patients' library opened in 1942. It was the dream of Mona Going, who was the Hospital Librarian for Kent, appointed in 1951.

She started her career as a volunteer at the Kent & Sussex Hospital in 1938, and she developed patient library services during the war while working as an ambulance driver for the Red Cross. She was instrumental in establishing reading therapy groups and introducing large print and talking books, and was awarded the OBE in 1977 for services to hospital libraries.

Two white papers were published looking at the NHS in 1971 and 1972, one concerned with seeking to get the mentally ill out of long-term institutions, the other with the joining up of community services still split between local authorities and the NHS.

Emmanuel Church was demolished by the Hospital Management Committee in 1974, and over 50 unidentified bodies were removed from the churchyard, where the main entrance road was constructed into the hospital, and reinterred at Tunbridge Wells Cemetery.

Mona Going OBE

Reorganisation

In 1974, The NHS was reorganised. The government's key point was that services should be provided by the NHS alone rather than by GP Committees and local authorities as well.

The Kent Area Health Authority was created with its HQ at Preston Hall near Maidstone. A new regional body, the South East Thames Regional Health Authority, oversaw the whole structure. New District Management Teams were created roughly on the same lines as the old Hospital Management Committees.

In Tunbridge Wells, a new Tunbridge Wells Health District Management Team was created at Sherwood Park. The Kent Area Health Authority was the largest AHA in the country, serving a population of over 1.4 million and employed over 27,400 staff.

Audrey Emerton moved to a new Regional Chief Nursing Officer post with Joy Young appointed as District Nursing Officer in March 1974.

In July 1974 the BMA and the Royal Colleges met the Government asking for more money for the NHS. They concluded that choices would have to be made about what could be afforded unless significant extra money was forthcoming.

A Royal Commission soon followed. However, the national economic situation, including the oil crisis, meant more NHS funding was unlikely.

The hospitals enjoyed a celebrity appearance by Racing Driver Jackie Stewart, who visited both Kent & Sussex Hospital and Pembury signing autographs in November.

The AHA took over services previously run by Kent County Council, including District Nurses, and The Ambulance Service. This led to the abolition of the Medical Officer for Health employed by local authorities. Community Medicine Specialists were employed by the Area Health Authorities to provide public health advice.

The Government felt that the reorganisation of 1974 provided coterminosity between local authorities and area health authorities, more involvement of clinicians in decision making and better use of resources.

After the election of May 1974, the Health Secretary, Barbara Castle, made the new government's policies clear: ending prescription charges, banning private practice and encouraging consultants to work full time for the NHS.

The economic situation was grim and so was NHS funding. The government was heading for a fight with both doctors and nurses. Consultants voted to start sanctions and nurses voted for strike action. National papers remarked the NHS was sinking into chaos.

The relationship between doctors and the government deteriorated and in January 1975 consultants started a work to rule. Later, junior doctors started action, leading Pembury to close to admissions until two consultants stepped in to keep casualty open.

A 30% pay rise was given to consultants to prevent an escalation of industrial unrest. However, a further escalation did go on, to prevent the government phasing out private beds in the NHS.

In early 1976, Audrey Emerton, as Chair of the Nurses League, wrote to members: *"With the bleak financial outlook for this year we all face a greater challenge ahead if nursing standards are to be maintained at a high level, and learners are to get a good training."*

In the Birthday Honours, Elizabeth Gravelius was given an OBE for services to the Red Cross as she retired from the post of Director.

In 1976, the country enjoyed a long hot summer. It was so hot that water shortages became a real problem, along with grass and heath fires. However, the year started on a very icy and cold note and on one icy February day 190 casualties were taken to Pembury with suspected fractures after falls on the ice.

Accident and Emergency

Accident services, which had been considered in the previous decade, came into focus again. It was clear that no new accident centre was going to be built at Tunbridge Wells in the immediate future, but something had to be done. The increase in road accidents and survivable cardiac conditions were putting a strain on services.

Things came to a head after the Community Health Council produced a report into casualty services in Tunbridge Wells, condemning them as inadequate. A leak to the Daily Mail produced a big page article in August 1975. The paper proclaimed: *"Be warned! Choose your day wisely if you crash near this hospital."*

It condemned the size of A&E and the inadequate facilities at Pembury, describing how in the event of a major accident: *"the day must come when the scene will be that of a dressing station in World War 1!"*

Sir Patrick Mayhew, the MP for Tunbridge Wells, raised the situation in the House of Commons.

A local appeal was launched and thousands of pounds flooded in from residents around Tunbridge Wells, enabling limited improvements to Casualty at both Pembury and the Kent & Sussex. The Courier published a 'Best Buys Casualty Shopping List' with the prices of equipment that needed to be purchased for the Casualty Departments. A public meeting organised by the Courier early in 1976 saw over 100 residents hear of the danger of oxygen pipes running across the floor from portable cylinders, and other condemned equipment still in use. Dr Loveday, who was actively involved in the campaign, remembered the Resuscitation Room was so small that one day a Junior Anaesthetist had to climb through the window to get to the head end of the trolley.

The A&E Department at Pembury after the expansion of the department.

The new departments opened at the end of December 1978. They were opened by Sir Eric Bradbury, the chair of the Community Health Council. He had been an ardent supporter of the fundraising and, as a former Surgeon Vice Admiral, knew what was needed. He knew, as did the staff who worked in them, that the improvements were only a temporary stopgap. At Pembury a new wooden hut was built onto the existing Casualty hut to give better facilities, including a resuscitation room, sluice and staff changing areas. At Kent & Sussex better waiting facilities and equipment modernised the departments.

Penny Scrimgeour, who was working out of Southborough Ambulance Station, remembered: *"We had a slide indicator sign in the station to remind crews which A&E was open and where we had to take patients! The old A&Es were so small and simply not fit for purpose. As soon as two ambulances were there they were full."*

Opening of the new Kent & Sussex A&E Department

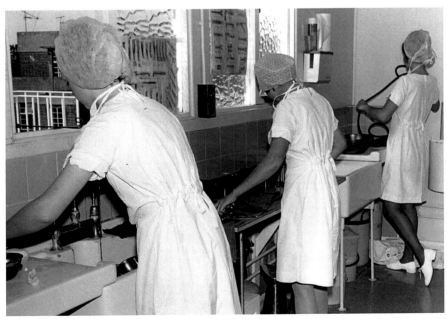

Washing Instruments in Honeywell Theatres – Kent & Sussex Hospital in 1977

More Change

In 1979, the Royal Commission on the NHS gave its findings to the new government. They led to further restructuring and more reports into the management of the service. The Griffiths Report into NHS management reported in 1983, urging a more businesslike approach with General Management being introduced.

As the NHS celebrated its 30th birthday in 1978, the economic situation in the country was increasingly bad. Inflation was rampant and industrial unrest was rife. It was clear no major capital works would be approved.

Nurses and other health workers reacted angrily to a government decision to make doctors a special case and award a them pay rise - but not nurses. The following winter became known as the Winter of Discontent, and industrial action across the NHS increased.

That Winter some services were hit by industrial action, including that by ancillary staff in January 1979 along with ambulance staff and radiographers. Other staff manned protest and picket lines in their spare time. The dispute by tanker drivers also affected the hospital, leading to the isolation of heating in all but patient care areas. Staff in other areas had to work in their coats with no heating until the dispute was ended. Ambulance staff joined the dispute in 1980, and police and volunteers stepped in to provide basic emergency cover.

It was in this year that the World Health Organisation finally declared the world free from smallpox. This disease was one of the main reasons behind establishing the Tunbridge Wells infirmary, and it marked a major achievement in public health.

The Tunbridge Wells Maternity Home was closed in 1978 and eventually converted into accommodation for geriatric patients. The new building was called Highlands House and opened in March 1980, to enabling the closure of some wards at Kent & Sussex Hospital for an ambitious rebuilding programme.

In 1981 a new Badminton Hall and Sports Hall was opened at Pembury by the Marchioness of Abergavenny. This was part of a campaign by renowned Consultant Neville Gibson as part of the Social Club.

Dr Mike Everest said: *"Neville Gibson's contribution to the life of the hospitals was huge. He took a great interest in the life of the hospitals, and his ability to spearhead a campaign was immense. New theatres, A&E, Swimming Pool - whatever it was he was there!"*

Reorganisation

The Regional Health Authority published its report 'Towards a More Responsive Service' in 1980, looking at restructuring across the South East Thames area. It found there were too many tiers, too many administrators, and a failure to make decisions effectively, thus wasting money.

It pointed out that Tunbridge Wells managed East Grinstead even though the latter was in the South West Thames Area, and Leybourne Grange even though it was in Maidstone District. It pointed out that Crowborough was in Eastbourne District but managed by Tunbridge Wells. It found that although Tunbridge Wells managed hospitals it didn't manage community services across borders, and it felt a merger between Tunbridge Wells and Maidstone Health Districts was to be considered.

The proposals were largely put to one side as a result of further reorganisation in 1982, when the Area Health Authority was abolished. In its place, the District Management Teams were converted into District Health Authorities in their own right. The Tunbridge Wells District Health Authority based themselves at Sherwood Park.

The economic challenges of the country saw unions unite to reject a 6.4% pay offer and go on to another dispute with the Government, eventually settling on 6.5%. Nurses in Tunbridge Wells pledged not to strike but to man picket lines and protest in their breaks and off duty periods. The largest picket was at the gates of Pembury Hospital.

On the night of 30th January 1981, an arson attack on the nurses' home at the Kent & Sussex Hospital saw fifty nurses evacuated, and considerable damage to Burslem House ground floor.

The economic crisis meant that talk of a new hospital subsided. Although the hospital was old the staff loved the environment at Pembury. Margaret Barnden, who was a Casualty Sister, said: *"There are many memories of Pembury but I remember the sheer hard work that went on. Often porters would manually push patients from the bottom wards up the hill outside to the top of the site to theatres or X-ray in all weathers. I remember holding an umbrella over patients when it was raining!"*

Emmanuel Church, which was demolished to make way for new access road and expansion of the Kent & Sussex Hospital site. The Kent & Sussex exit can be seen alongside the church

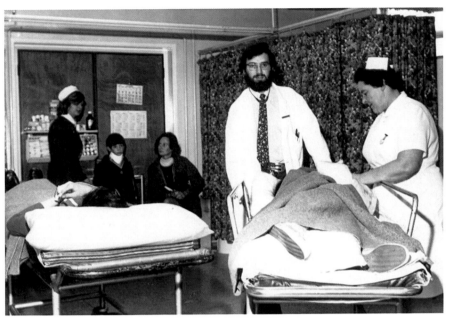

A&E at Kent & Sussex Hospital showing poor facilities

Opening of the Library at Kent & Sussex

THE CHAIRMAN AND MEMBERS OF THE
TUNBRIDGE WELLS AND LEYBOURNE HOSPITAL MANAGEMENT COMMITTEE

request the pleasure of the company of

Dr. and Mrs. T.S. Leedham

at a

COCKTAIL PARTY

on

Friday, 22nd March, 1974, at 7.00 p.m.

at

SHERWOOD PARK

R.S.V.P. on enclosed card
by 15th March

Black Tie or Lounge Suits

Marking the end of the Hospital Management Committee and the start of the era of the Area Health Authority

Sandhill staff residences at Pembury 1979

Christmas on the wards at Pembury in the 1970s

HM Queen Elizabeth the Queen Mother visiting Pembury in 1977

Opening of the new Nurse Education Centre at Pembury in 1972
Audrey Emerton with Dame Muriel Powell

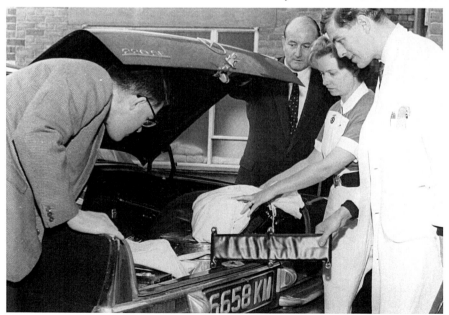

Medical & Nursing Staff inspect the new Obstetric Flying Squad Equipment at Pembury in 1974

Tunbridge Wells & Leybourne
Hospital Management Committee

*The final meeting of No. 1 House Committee will
be held at Pembury Hospital on*

Thursday 28th March 1974.

*The Chairman and members have pleasure in inviting you to
take tea with them in the Nurses' Home of Pembury Hospital
on that day between the hours of 3. 30 and 5 p.m.*

R.S.V.P.

Divisional Manager

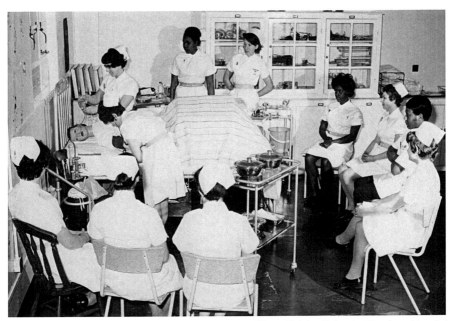

Nurse Training School at Pembury Hospital

The view from the roof of the Kent & Sussex Hospital across Tunbridge Wells – the wall is the original boundary wall of the Culverden Mansion that stood on the sites

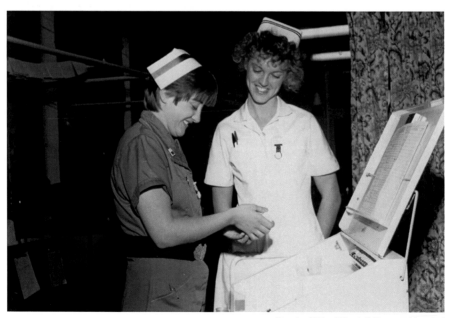

Surgical Ward Kent & Sussex Hospital

Chapter 9

1982 – 1994 Trust Us – it's all change!

Following the 1982 reorganisation and the abolition of the Kent Area Health Authority, the Tunbridge Wells Health Authority took over full management of health services in the area from its HQ in Sherwood Park.

Fire!

On the night 17th November, fire broke out in Amulree and Meyer Wards at Pembury Hospital. These wards were the old wartime wooden huts, and fire took hold quickly. 50 fire-fighters attended from all over West Kent, and five other wards were evacuated, including Brocklehurst, Howell, Leedham and Anderson Wards. The Fire Service paid tribute to the evacuation efforts and how disaster was averted.

Beryl Whiddett was preparing for night duty that evening and saw smoke from her house: *"I quickly called the staff I was expecting, then, with my husband, went to help. On my Gynaecology Unit we cleared a small area which was soon filled up with frightened old ladies all clutching their handbags to their chests. Unfortunately, they had all lost their wristbands so we had no idea who they were. It was a miracle no one died."*

David Nicholson, who was an administrator, was called in to help. He said: *"We evacuated 120 or 130 patients. Most were in the car park when I arrived. Lots of nursing staff and volunteers from the village arrived to help. There was real concern about the risk of explosion from gas and oxygen supplies exposed to the fire. After the fire I was tasked to go through the remains to find patients' property, but there was really nothing that could be saved."*

Liz Macaulay, who worked as a Night Sister, recalled being rung at home. When she arrived she described the work of volunteers and staff as 'terrific'. She pushed beds up the hill to the main block, alongside members of the public who had turned up to offer assistance: *"Just as we got all the patients inside and sheltered, the heavens opened and it poured with rain!"*

Ambulance Service

In 1983, seatbelts became compulsory in the UK, leading to a fall in serious injuries, head injuries in particular, in road traffic collisions. Jane Highland, who was a Staff Nurse on Intensive Care, recalled: *"We saw almost immediately a reduction in young fit patients following road traffic accidents on ICU."*

The ambulance service developed new treatments only ever seen in hospital, as paramedic training became widely available around the UK. A new national ambulance training scheme for ambulance staff was supported and launched by the Department of Health. No longer would ambulance staff simply scoop and run at an incident, but provide enhanced, expert care at the scene.

Penny Scrimgeour joined the Kent Ambulance Service in 1984: *"In those days there were only about five women on the road in the whole of Kent – in fact, we had to go to Police HQ and be kitted out with some parts of female police uniforms, as they hadn't got female ambulance uniforms. It was much quieter than today. We hardly ever went out to patients, as GPs went out. There was no sat nav and no response times – we got there as fast as we could. The emphasis was on taking the patient to hospital with minimal interventions. By the end of the decade it had changed to us bringing A&E to the roadside."*

By the end of the 1980s, paramedics began to appear in ambulances across the county.

"At first I was daunted by the extra responsibility and skills we had, and indeed the public were sometimes unsure about us using these new skills at first. We had increasingly better equipped vehicles, and were able to carry out many more skills at the incident - skills that were previously only ever seen in A&E."

Culverden Wing

The South East Regional Health Authority gave capital funding of over £7.5 million for a new wing at the Kent & Sussex Hospital, to centralise Surgery and A&E at Kent & Sussex. The Culverden Wing, as it was known, was intended to be only a temporary move until a district hospital could be constructed at Pembury or another site. The unit took four years to design and was constructed on the site of two wartime huts, which were demolished. These two wards, 1 and 3, were moved to Highlands House, recently refurbished after the closure of the maternity home. A further block was constructed for medical records and the medical secretariat, and opened in 1981.

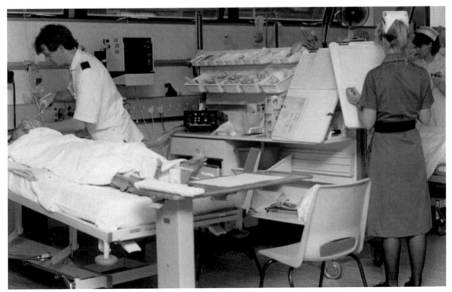

Intensive Care at the Kent & Sussex Hospital in 1987

The new unit brought a purpose-built intensive care unit, restaurant, mortuary, physiotherapy unit and accident and emergency department. When it opened in 1985 the A&E Department at Pembury was closed and all A&E centralised in Tunbridge Wells. While surgery and orthopaedics were based at Kent & Sussex, medicine was still separated between the two hospitals. Each week a different unit would be on take, the old A&E being converted into an acute admissions unit.

Throughout early 1985 local groups and staff were offered the chance to see the new building prior to its opening. The new wing was opened on 1st November by Norman Fowler, the Minister for Social Services. He said that he found the new unit to be 'fantastic!'.

The new A&E department saw a change in the management of emergencies with the appointment of the first A&E Consultant, Jim Walker, in March 1985. He had previously studied tropical medicine, having worked in Rwanda, Switzerland and Jamaica. He spent time in A&E at the London Hospital. During his time at Tunbridge Wells he introduced trauma teams and worked to introduce advanced trauma life support courses.

Penny Scrimgeour, who was working at Southborough Ambulance Station at the time, remembered he was held in high esteem and affection by the Ambulance Crews: *"He always found the time to talk to ambulance crews, and the introduction of ATLS was such an advance in managing trauma patients."*

Janis Marns, who was a sister in the new unit, said: *"It was quite revolutionary working in a purpose-built accident & emergency department, with so much space and facilities such as a plaster room and theatre."*

The effect of centralising all acute services at the Kent & Sussex was not universally welcomed, and a report to the Authority in 1984 revealed morale at Pembury was getting worse amongst staff and urgent action was necessary.

Culverden Wing
Courtesy of Historical and interesting views of Tunbridge wells by Katharina Mahler-Bech

Phase 2 of the Kent & Sussex changes saw the conversion of the old dining room to an outpatients unit, and a dental and endoscopy unit built in the old casualty unit. The huts were then upgraded to form a three-ward orthopaedic unit along with a psychiatric unit.

Above the new physiotherapy unit and next to ICU, was the new Ward 16, an acute admissions ward. Patients were transferred to Ward 16 at night rather than disturb a ward, and then moved to their ward the next morning. Patients from theatres were again moved to Ward 16 post-surgery. Margaret Barnden, a Sister who escorted the Secretary of State when he officially opened the new unit, said: *"It was a great concept but increasingly it became gridlocked as more beds were taken for waiting-list patients, and Ward 16 got subsumed into general beds."*

Penny Scrimgeour said: *"We were very proud of our new A&E, and ambulance crews had an excellent relationship with the staff there."*

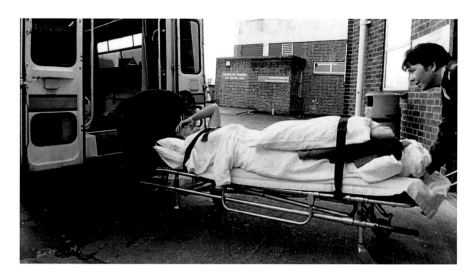

Management

In 1983, the Griffiths Enquiry recommended that a single officer manage a part of each service, and so each part of the service was divided into units with a Unit General Manager in charge, reporting to the District General Manager. Annette Sergeant, who would later come to Pembury as Chief Executive, was working in London at the time.

The Kent & Sussex Hospital. The building in the foreground was the Cardiac Catheter Lab and just behind is the Medical Secretaries and Records building

She said: *"It made management more accountable, and an individual was responsible rather than consensus and committee. The public, who often thought of the NHS as full of faceless bureaucrats, had a real person to hold to account."*

Jack Lowe was appointed as District General Manager for Tunbridge Wells in 1986. With his background in industry he called on his experience to create a new management structure for Tunbridge Wells. The district was divided into four units, the acute unit, community unit, mental handicap unit and Queen Victoria Unit. A new District Management Team at Sherwood Park would be formed into an Executive Board.

The first two unit general managers were John Evans for the Acute side and Maureen Packwood for the Community side.

The increase in the use of technology saw the establishment of a District Electro-mechanical Engineering Unit or EME for short in 1983.

In 1986, waiting time for Orthopaedics for a first appointment was 40 weeks and rising, against service reductions to save money. A new divisional structure was introduced with Divisional Managers for Surgery, Maternity, Medical and Orthopaedics.

New Hospital?
After building work started on the new Culverden Wing, attention was redoubled to try to get a single-site district general hospital financed. The Health Authority prioritised a shortlist of options for the Regional Health Authority. These were:

1. Single Site: Pembury

2. Single Site: Sherwood Park

3. Split Site: Acute at K&S

4. Single Site: K&S

The District Health Authority recommended to the Regional Health Authority that an option to build a new District General Hospital on the Pembury Site should be followed through.

It was on 13th May 1988 that the Courier proudly announced: 'Go-ahead for new hospital' based on a single-site Pembury Hospital. This followed an announcement made at a League of Friends meeting by the Health Authority. It explained it was 10 years away but they were hopeful it would be delivered on time. Time of course was the judge, and 10 years later they were still fighting for it!

Hawkenbury Hospital, the old Tunbridge Wells District Isolation Hospital, closed its doors in 1983 and patients were moved to Pembury.

The financial situation was getting worse as the 1980s drew to a close. The Courier reported that in July 1990 only emergency admissions were being accepted at both hospitals. Later, in November, A&E was on divert to other hospitals as no beds could be found.

HIV and AIDS

Perhaps the biggest health issue of the 1980s was the discovery of Acquired Immune Deficiency Syndrome (AIDS) at the start of the decade. The further discovery of the HIV virus as the cause, and how it was spread, saw a huge public health campaign.

Every part of the NHS would be affected as the spread of the virus was understood. Gloves became a routine part of every procedure, and training and awareness was pushed out to all staff over the decade. The safety of blood products became an issue leading to the introduction of screening in 1985 and heat treatment a year later.

Progress

One of the main advances of the late 1980s was the availability of minimal access surgery. Arthroscopic washout and examination of knee joints and Trans-urethral resection of bladder tumours were common, but the techniques spread widely, meaning a reduction in hospital stays and an increase in day-care surgery.

Jane Highland, who started work on the old Intensive Care Unit, moved into the new ICU when it opened as part of the Culverden Wing, recalled: *"Intensive Care quickly became much more high tech – more invasive monitoring. We also started using clot busting drugs like streptokinase."*

She revealed that the new technology was not universally accepted: *"There was some scepticism about Intensive Care, but the fact was we were really saving lives."*

Marion Goldsmith, who had become a Night Sister and a keen advocate of extended nursing roles such as venepuncture and intravenous antibiotics administration, male catheterisation and others, began training around the hospital: *"We had a chance to give a faster and better service to our patients, and this meant fewer delays and speedier diagnosis and treatments, and although some people resented the new skills I really felt it was better for patients,"* she said.

Ghost
Pembury Hospital made the national news in the autumn of 1985 when three nurses all claimed they had seen a ghost while on night duty. The Bishop of Rochester's Adviser on the Paranormal, Rev Peter Thomas, went to the hospital. A special 40-minute service was held by the hospital chaplain to lay the spirits to rest. The Sun newspaper proclaimed: 'Bed ghost panned!' and the Courier's front page said: 'Priest cleanses haunted ward'. Many people wrote in with their experiences of ghosts at Pembury.

The old outpatients department at Pembury was upgraded and revamped. The building was still a remnant of the workhouse days when it used to house tramps. The first plans to revamp were drawn up in 1960 and quietly dropped.

The busy entrance to Pembury Hospital claimed another victim in April 1988 when a man crossing the road from the bus stops was killed.

Financial cutbacks
The financial situation was getting worse as the 1980s drew to a close. The courier reported that in July 1990 only emergency admissions were being accepted at both hospitals. Later in November A&E was on divert to other hospitals as no beds could be found.

In 1987, four Consultant Surgeons, Mr Bentley, Mr Ford, Mr Williams and Mr Lewis, wrote to The Times to condemn the cuts to services. They pointed out that the reductions in waiting lists they had worked hard to achieve would be a waste as the Health Authority was stopping all but essential surgery and closing wards half way through the financial year. They argued that government policy is seen as a bid to force more patients into the private sector. The following week Jack Lowe, the District General Manager, wrote to the Times supporting the consultants, even saying that they underestimated the problems.

Later in the year, consultants and managers met with Tunbridge Wells MP Sir Patrick Mayhew in what was described as a constructive 90-minute exchange of views. He agreed to talk to the Minister.

Inpatient beds at the Homeopathic Hospital were closed in September 1987 and moved to Pembury, leaving the Homeopathic to be an outpatients hospital. The closure of the Sevenoaks Maternity Unit soon followed in a series of cost-cutting measures. Later that year the Acute Unit's overspend led to further reductions, including the closure of Ward 16 and a surgical ward at the Kent & Sussex Hospital.

In a further round of publicity the Courier, in an article on increased waiting times, carried a quote from the Chairman of the Consultants Committee Dr Robin Loveday, in which he alleged that patients not suffering from life threatening conditions stood little chance, if any, of being admitted to a Tunbridge Wells Hospital before the next financial year.

The financial cutbacks were causing closures and service suspensions, leading consultants and managers to oppose them publicly at the start of 1989.

Mr Gordon Hill, Consultant at Pembury, spoke on behalf of the medical staff accusing the Government of misleading the public about the amount of money that was available for the two hospitals.

The settlement of £1.6 billion would not be an increase in real terms. John Evans for the management said that so many economy measures had been taken in the previous ten years that further cost-cutting would seriously affect patient care. The Courier revealed that 17 beds had been closed at Kent & Sussex - the Admissions Unit and 3 ICU beds.

In early January 1990 the financial situation deteriorated dramatically, and the hospitals were put on an emergency footing, cancelling all elective surgery and agency staff. At the same time an appeal was made to increase the number of private patients at Kent & Sussex. This met with strong disapproval from the District Consultants Committee who, whilst agreeing with the position of the Authority, felt unable to approve the increase in private work whilst cancelling elective operations. The chairman wrote: *"There is widespread astonishment and resentment at the recommendation that, at the same time as cancelling all elective surgery, we should be actively encouraged to do private, non-urgent surgery in NHS Hospitals."*

Constant attempts were made to reduce costs including closing casualty units in community at night, closing surgical units and theatres at community hospitals, and reducing elective admissions to the Acute Unit. Havelock Ward was closed in 1992 to try to balance the books, along with a reduction in the number of surgical beds.

Nurse shortages

Nurse shortages became acute throughout early 1988, beds had to be closed and elective surgery cancelled. In May 1986, the United Kingdom Central Council for Nursing published a new proposal for nurse training, including a more academic-based training linked to universities. Its title was Project 2000, a name that would not quickly be forgotten by the nursing profession due to the equal numbers of opponents and supporters.

A two-bedded High Dependency Unit was opened at Pembury in 1986 next to Amelia Scott Ward, and was named the Neville Gibson Unit.

It's an ill wind

A blizzard brought in 1987 and continued through much of January and into February, causing significant disruption to services with many rural areas cut off. There were many stories of staff walking to patients, and staff sleeping in the hospitals for several days to keep services running.

Many of the staff at the hospital went to bed having been reassured by Michael Fish that a hurricane was not on the way. In the early hours of 16th October they woke to the sound of crashing roof tiles and no electricity or telephones.

No-one who was there will forget it, especially that morning's theatre staff at Pembury, who were called out to attend theatres where a sick patient needed surgery. They fought through roads blocked by trees and power lines. Other staff who were not on-call came in as they lived nearer. Mr Bamford, Consultant Obstetrician, and John Evans wrote to the theatre staff to thank them for their efforts that night.

From 8.00am that morning 70% of admissions for the first 12 hours were from the hurricane and 48 hours later the hospital had admitted 120 casualties, including 16 chainsaw accidents, 24 flying glass incidents and several paraffin stove burns. Although both hospitals had emergency generators, many staff had no power at home for several days and in some cases weeks.

The Pembury Fete in 1990 was opened by Louise Jameson and raised over £10,000.

Tunbridge Wells Health District

Sherwood Park, Pembury Road, Tunbridge Wells, Kent. TN2 3QE

Telephone (0892) 38811

Tunbridge Wells Health District Logo

A bus Accident near East Grinstead, involving a number of troops, tested the Major Incident Plan at the Kent & Sussex Hospital in May 1988. The report concluded that all had gone well.

At the Conservative Party Conference in autumn 1987 the Health Minister, John Moore, pledged the complete reform of the NHS. Many in the NHS were weary of reform but equally aware that things could not carry on as they were.

In 1989 the national ambulance strike saw St John Ambulance, Red Cross and troops on the streets providing emergency services.

The nurse regrading system brought in during 1988/9 led to a huge amount of disquiet and appeals, especially by senior nurses. Nurses were graded from A to I depending on skills and responsibility.

Rainbow Ward

In the summer of 1987, amid the financial crisis, Rainbow Ward opened its doors. The new Children's Ward on the top floor of the Kent & Sussex Hospital was considered a revolutionary design and won admirers from across the country. It was part of a package of improvements known as Phase II of the Kent & Sussex Redevelopment, following the opening of the Culverden Wing.

The official opening was performed by the Nicholas Scott, the Social Security Minister, in September 1987. He had been a Northern Ireland minister previously and, at the height of the IRA bombing campaign, the police were being particularly security-conscious. A car parked outside A&E caused a security alert and the police called in the Bomb Squad. Before they arrived a night staff nurse admitted it was hers and the alert was stood down minutes before the Minister arrived.

The Duchess of Kent visited to see the facilities in April 1988 and spent time on Rainbow, even signing plaster casts on children in the ward.

CT Scanner

A public appeal to buy a CT scanner for Pembury Hospital was launched with the support of the Courier. The new scanner opened at Pembury in 1988.

TUNBRIDGE WELLS HEALTH AUTHORITY

The Chairman has great pleasure in inviting

....

*to the formal opening of the Phase II Development
of the Kent and Sussex Hospital*

by

Nicholas Scott MBE JP MP

*at 11.00 a.m. on Thursday 3rd September 1987
in the Staff Restaurant, Kent and Sussex Hospital*

*Secretary to the Authority
Sherwood Park, Pembury Road,
Tunbridge Wells, Kent TN2 3QE*   *RSVP*

The appeal became legendary - it captured the imagination of the public, and the new scanner was the most up-to-date outside London. It highlighted the need for a single-site hospital, however, as patients in A&E had to be taken by ambulance to Pembury for scans after head injuries and then moved back.

In 1989 an agreement was signed by Peter Baldwin, Chairman of the South East Thames Health Authority, to create an air ambulance service. The service, originally only part-time, began to fly with charitable funding 7 days a week.

Only London and Cornwall had air ambulance services at the time. Penny Scrimgeour was amongst the first crew on board, and was the first female to crew the Kent Air Ambulance: *"It was a stressful job as we were flying to serious calls all the time, but we saw tremendous variety of work and certainly made a difference to patients."*

A new hospital?

Another attempt to look at a new hospital was made in 1988, with the District General Manager chairing a group to look at a new-build and the options. The authority was able to sell off surplus property but lacked the permission to do so.

The Government move to increase competition and efficiency required catering, domestic and laundry services to be put out to tender to ensure value for money. This caused a great deal of concern amongst staff.

The decision to close the Radiotherapy Unit in 1984 and transfer to Maidstone was greeted with mass public protest. A deputation even went to Health Minister Edwina Currie, but in January 1989, Health Secretary Ken Clarke announced the final closure of the Radiotherapy Unit at Pembury and its move to Maidstone Hospital. The monumental battle to save the unit had dominated the news for over three years, and succeeded in gaining massive support.

In 1993, the final radiotherapy moves were made to Maidstone. Psychiatry at Kent & Sussex moved over to Pembury at the end of 1993 and made room for a Medical Ward at Kent & Sussex, thus centralising acute medicine at the Kent & Sussex Hospital for the first time. The old Ward 16 admissions Unit, closed since 1989, was converted into a Coronary Care Unit.

In 1985 the Tunbridge Wells Health Authority published its strategic plan, stating that: *"There is an overriding need to provide a District General Hospital on one site.*

The view from the top of 'F' Block at Pembury. it was from this roof that Dr Grasby saw the attack on the naval base at Chatham in WWII, and watched the Battle of Britain

From the top of Woodlands House looking at the old Radiotherapy building in B Block, newly turned into an Ophthalmology Unit

In January 1989, the Courier revealed that the Health Authority was pressing ahead with a new hospital at Pembury. It finally excluded Sherwood Park on cost grounds and Kent & Sussex as too crowded. It revealed that bed numbers would have to fall to make it viable, but that a new hospital would be built within five years. Once again, time was to judge this!

The NHS and Community Care Act 1990 established the framework by which NHS Trusts would be formed to run the NHS, with the first wave of Trusts arriving in 1991. It introduced purchaser and provider roles and the internal market. GPs were offered the chance to become fund holders who could buy services from other providers, not just the local hospital. Change in the NHS was forthcoming with the advent of NHS Trusts.

The Government believed that having local self governing trusts rather than health authorities was the way forward.

During 1993, financial restrictions were once again in place. The Authority, having met its waiting list targets half way through the year, closed Ward 7 and Honeywell Theatres for the rest of the financial year to save money.

At Tunbridge Wells, the Community and Acute Unit combined and put forward a bid in the third wave to become a trust but this was rejected, and a separate bid, which was approved in 1994, saw the creation of a community trust based at Blackhurst and an acute trust based at Pembury Hospital. Statutory Instrument number 163, laid before Parliament on 28th January 1994, came into force on 8th February, and so from 1st April the Kent & Sussex Weald NHS Trust came into being. A further order created the Weald of Kent Community NHS Trust, looking after Community Services.

Changes to nurse education, as part of Project 2000, meant the Nurse Education Centre became part of the University of Brighton in 1993.

So we end this chapter as we started, in a period of change and reorganisation in the NHS.

The Minister arrives to open the new Culverden Wing

The minister talks to the A&E Sisters at the opening of Culverden Wing in 1985

The Minister at the opening of the Phase II work at Kent & Sussex Hospital in 1987

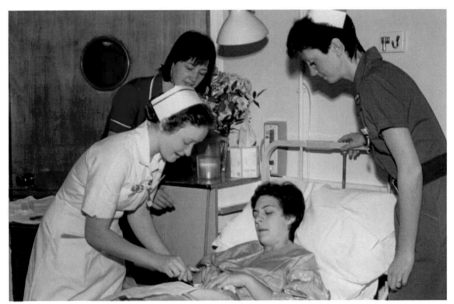

Hands on Training at The Kent & Sussex Hospital

New uniforms: The 1980s saw the end of aprons, the 1990s would see the end of caps and widespread use of uniform trouser suits

The old radiotherapy unit in B Block at Pembury

The water tower – demolished in the late 1980s

A BETTER PLACE TO GET BETTER

You'll recover in ideal surroundings if you choose the privacy and comfort of the splendid new Hargraves Suite at the Kent & Sussex Hospital. There's really nowhere better to get better; and the finest possible medical facilities are all immediately to hand.

Opening very soon, the Hargraves Suite has been designed and equipped to lavish standards. Each of its nine single rooms has the kind of facilities you would expect in a luxury hotel, with service to match.

There's also a larger room with four beds offering the same standard of service. You might consider this room if you are having only minor treatment; and there are special rates for day care patients.

LET US SPOIL YOU A LITTLE!

Our pleasure is in the service we give and in making your stay as comfortable and relaxing as possible. You have a shower en-suite, colour television, radio, telephone and a call system for personal attention whenever you need it.

Choose your meals from a daily menu that's designed to tempt you. Have a glass or two of wine when you feel like it. Order your usual daily newspaper. Make an appointment with the hairdresser. Send your clothes to the dry cleaner.

BEST POSSIBLE MEDICAL CARE

Most importantly, staying as a patient in the Hargraves Suite you will benefit from the fine medical skills and nursing care for which the Kent & Sussex is known, with every kind of expertise and advanced technology to hand.

Our operating theatres are equipped to the highest NHS standards and staffed by dedicated personnel. Specialist and general diagnostic services are available day and night. The comprehensive laboratory service provides a complete range of pathology investigations in haematology, clinical chemistry, histology, microbiology and cervical cytology.

Patients in the Hargraves Suite also have access to the CAT scanner and nuclear medicine department at Pembury Hospital. And if necessary the intensive therapy unit at the Kent & Sussex Hospital provides a vital service that very few small private hospitals can offer.

SO MUCH DIFFERENCE

This very pleasant, restful environment can make so much difference to recuperation. It combines the best of medical skill and attention with extremely comfortable and well-serviced private rooms. For more information and details of charges, please ask for a copy of our brochure.

Advert for The Hargraves Suite in The Kent & Sussex Hospital

216

Chapter 10

1994 - 2000 - A new hospital looms

On 1st April 1994, the Kent & Sussex Weald NHS Trust came into being, taking over the Acute Unit of Tunbridge Wells Health Authority.

John Evans, its first Chief Executive, appointed a Trust Board to manage the new organisation, which was organised around Clinical Directorates led by a Clinical Director and a Business Manager.

Its journey to being a Trust was not easy. There were objections from all quarters, but finally the decision from the Department of Health came: the trust could go ahead. Judy Clabby recalled: *"It was all a bit of a rush – we had only a few weeks to get everything ready, including designing a logo, appointing staff, fixing budgets, organising property and, not least, arranging standing orders and finance. It was becoming a worry whether we'd have the budget to carry out the service."*

Mr Philip Bentley was the first Medical Director of the Trust, before being succeeded by Mr Jim Lewis. Margaret Jones-Evans became Director of Nursing and Judy Clabby Trust Secretary.

At the end of the first year, despite fears over finances and a 3.8 million under-fund, the Trust balanced its books. Pressures were becoming apparent however, with a backlog of maintenance bills and initiatives like the New Deal for junior doctors increasing expenditure.

The new trust kept a new hospital at the forefront of its mind, but the climate had changed and a PFI - or Private Finance Initiative - was the only way to secure the funding. The trust put forward a bid in 1996 to secure funding for a £42M hospital. The Courier proudly announced that a new hospital could be built by the year 2000. The bid was turned down, to much disappointment from staff and stakeholders alike.

In 1996, John Evans retired from the Trust and, after a short while with Deputy Chief Executive Bernard Quinn at the helm, Annette Sergeant took over as Chief Executive, she recalled the case for a new hospital was very apparent. She said: *"I was shocked by the state of repair of the estate, especially patient accommodation. It was clear that there had been under-investment and something had to be done.*

It became apparent that bids had not been realistic or affordable, and there were other equally compelling and strong bids for finance. What we had to do was recognise the changing NHS, and make our bid able to stand up to scrutiny. For instance, we had to recognise inpatient bed numbers would reduce due to an increase in day-case surgery and shorter inpatient-stays, because of more effective surgical techniques."

It was decided that a considerable amount of work would be needed on a new PFI bid, and that collaboration with other stakeholders would be paramount, as well as an understanding of the strategic priorities of the West Kent Health Authority. There were wider changes to the way health care was commissioned and it was clear that not every service would be commissioned in every hospital. The new Chief Executive recognised the need for more involvement of clinicians in management and tried to increase their involvement - a move welcomed by consultants. There was also a focus on staff engagement, with well-attended open staff meetings.

Clinical Nurse Managers at the Kent & Sussex Hospital 1999

A new Renal Unit was opened in the old casualty building at Pembury. The facility was named after Dr Arnold Osman, who brought the first renal unit to Pembury after the war. It was opened by his widow in July 1996.

In 1997 a new government was elected, with the NHS a major election topic. A clear focus from the new government was on what was important to patients. There was recognition of under-funding, and an increase in investment was welcomed. There was, however, a series of targets imposed - many of which had funding attached. Waiting times were one of the first targets imposed on the trust, and action on A&E trolley-waits soon followed.

The Trust put forward a new PFI bid based on the Pembury Site after extensive consultation in early 1998. This followed a Board-to-Board meeting between the West Kent Health Authority and the Kent & Sussex Weald NHS Trust Board.

There was a big emphasis on the fact that Tunbridge Wells operated the only split-site acute service in the region, with a dossier of 600 examples showing how care had been compromised due to split-site working and poor-quality fabric of existing estate.

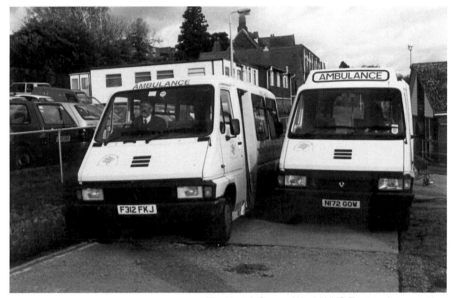

The Kent & Sussex Weald NHS Trust took over patient transport services from the ambulance service

The West Kent Health Authority strongly supported the bid, and so did partner agencies. However, support was not strong from Mid Kent Healthcare Trust, who ran Maidstone Hospital at the time. The WKHA required some options to go into the Strategic Outline case, including separating emergency and elective activity with Maidstone.

Local MPs were very supportive, and the Courier newspaper embarked on a massive campaign publishing thousands of postcards for the public to send to the Department of Health showing poor fabric and bearing the slogan: "Wish you were here?"

Lucy Johnson was a Staff Nurse on Ward 7, and went to the Houses of Parliament. She recalled: *"The politicians really did listen to us, and were interested in the conditions on the wards which we had to endure every day."*

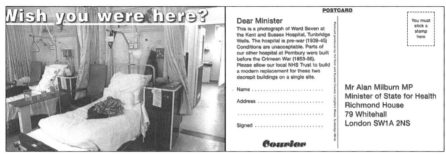

POSTCARD

Dear Minister

This is a photograph of Ward Seven at the Kent and Sussex Hospital, Tunbridge Wells. The hospital is pre-war (1939-45). Conditions are unacceptable. Parts of our other hospital at Pembury were built before the Crimean War (1853-56). Please allow our local NHS Trust to build a modern replacement for these two decrepit buildings on a single site.

Name ....

Address ....

....

Signed ....

You must stick a stamp here

Mr Alan Milburn MP
Minister of State for Health
Richmond House
79 Whitehall
London SW1A 2NS

Postcards

Local MPs with Ward 7 Nurses take a giant postcard to the Houses of Parliament

By early September 1998 the Courier had given away over 20,000 postcards for the public to send to the Minister.

However, on 7th April 1998 the PFI bid was turned down by the Health Minister Alan Milburn. In his press statement he said:
"It is not the end of the road for the Trust and its bid."

Margaret Barnden, who was Sister in Endoscopy at the time, recalled:
"We were so disappointed at the decision – we really did think we could get a new hospital. The fabric of the Kent & Sussex was just getting worse and areas had become not fit for purpose."

Tunbridge Wells MP Archie Norman was more direct in his House of Commons press release.
"There are strong suspicions that another agenda lies behind today's announcement. The new politically-correct view in the NHS is that hospitals should be merged. It may be that the real agenda is to force the merger with Maidstone, and gradually run down services in our area. Such an agenda is unacceptable to the people of Tunbridge Wells. More and more patients will have to travel further."

The trust redoubled its efforts with West Kent Health Authority to put forward a further bid at the end of 1998. However, on 7th July 1999 Annette Sergeant wrote to staff:
"It is with great sadness and regret that I am writing to advise you ministers have not agreed to our proposals to build a new hospital in Tunbridge Wells at present."

Claire Spence, who was Clinical Nurse Manager for Surgery at the time, recalled:
"So much effort had gone into the bid and the news was devastating for us."

Many staff and most members of the public could not understand why the Government kept refusing permission for a new hospital and the realisation that closer ties with Maidstone might mean loss of some services from Tunbridge Wells led to a feeling of uncertainty across the trust.

On a daily basis staff were having to make do by providing care in substandard decaying buildings.

The Minister did agree to visit the trust to see for himself just what conditions were like. At his visit he saw the crumbling Pembury Hospital and the traffic conditions between sites. He then wrote to MPs stating: *"The case for doing something is inescapable."*

At the end of July, Baroness Hayman wrote to Chairman Mary Symes as Trust Chairman, confirming that consultation would go ahead on merging Kent & Sussex Weald and Mid Kent NHS Trusts.

View of the huts at Pembury from the roof of Woodlands House

It became clear that no PFI would be granted without closer ties, with the Mid Kent Trust running Maidstone Hospital and the rationalisation and sharing of services across West Kent. A Statutory Consultation began on 26th July 1999, running through the autumn, on merging the two trusts to create one acute Trust.

In the summer of 1999 staff at the Kent & Sussex practised their response to a train crash as they were woken at 6 am for the practice incident.
The hospital was given a clean bill of health by the Regional Advisor watching the proceedings.

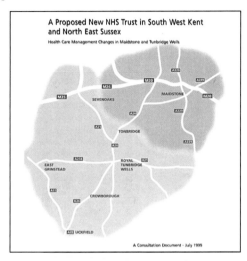

Consultation Document

In April 1999, the Trust received funding from the Princess Diana fund to create a Diana Nursing Team in West Kent, based at Pembury to look after sick children at home.

Further investment saw a new Pathology Laboratory opened at Pembury in September 1999.

Later in 1999, the trust received money to upgrade the A&E Department at the Kent & Sussex Hospital, which led to the creation of an Acute Assessment Unit built in the old Physiotherapy Department, and the creation of two additional resuscitation bays. Physiotherapy then moved to Ward 4, an empty hut at Kent & Sussex.

In 1999, a patient died after receiving a wrong blood transfusion, and the Trust was fined over £7,000 under the Health & Safety At Work Act. This led to a change in the way blood was administered.

In 1997, the Board agreed to market-test hotel and support services, and after a tendering Medirest were given the contract for cleaning and catering services. Annette Sergeant said: *"There was concern about market-testing services, but the private sector was able to bring new facilities and investment to services which the NHS could not achieve at that time."*

The view from Theatres at Pembury looking at 'B' Block and the lawns towards Woodlands House

The Minister talks to Medical Director Jim Lewis and Chairman Mary Symes, with local MPs listening, during his tour of the Trust estate

Judy Clabby reveals peeling paint and water damage at Pembury Hospital to the Courier

Poster supporting the new hospital campaign

*The A&E Department at the Kent & Sussex Hospital in 1995.
Mr J Walker, A&E Consultant, with staff*

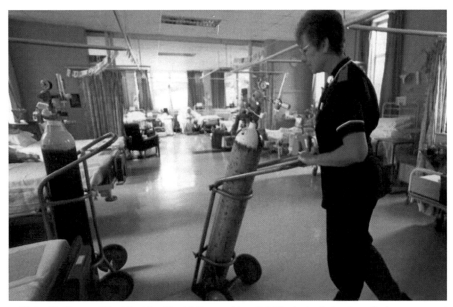

*Sister Lin Eyre on Ward 9 at the Kent & Sussex Hospital. The lack of piped medical gases meant
staff had to wheel heavy cylinders of oxygen around the ward. 1996*

*Staff gather outside the Kent & Sussex Hospital in 1994 to
mark 60 years of the Kent & Sussex Hospital*

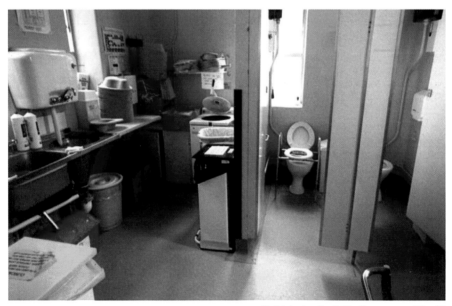

Outdated patients' bathrooms on Ward 9

Chapter 11

2000 - 2012

Brave New World

After the Millennium celebrations had subsided, the merger between Kent & Sussex Weald NHS Trust and Mid Kent NHS Trust was agreed, and on 1st April 2000 the new Maidstone & Tunbridge Wells NHS Trust was formed. The new trust ran services from Preston Hall, Kent County Ophthalmic Hospital and Maidstone General as well as Pembury and the Kent & Sussex Hospitals. A new executive team was appointed under Chairman Anne Chapman and Chief Executive Stephen Collinson. The new trust retained its headquarters at Pembury Hospital. A new organisational structure centred on care groups headed by general managers was introduced.

The government published its long-awaited NHS plan in the summer of 2000. For the first time the NHS had a clear ten-year plan, with investment attached and performance requirements. At its launch the Government described the NHS as 'a 1940s system in a 21st century world'.

The end of 2000 was overshadowed by severe floods and a fuel strike, which threatened to affect the ability of the Trust to continue to provide services. However, contingency plans meant all emergency services were able to continue.

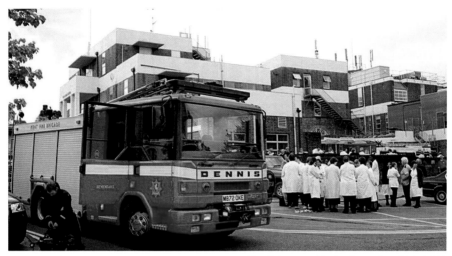
Fire fighters tackle the fire on Level 6 in 2002

A&E waiting times

Across the country waiting times in A&E departments had increased significantly, partly as a result of changes in out-of-hours GP provision and partly because of changing expectations. NHS trusts, too, had to balance the targets for elective operations on which they were measured, which often led to patients waiting in A&E for beds taken by elective patients.

Since 1994, Community Health Councils had carried out casualty watches which reported on the length of time patients had been waiting in A&E departments. This had become a national hot topic.

The Tunbridge Wells Community Health Council reported the longest wait in Kent & Sussex was 24 hours and 4 minutes in 1995, but the longest wait for a bed in 1999 was 49 hours.

The Government, aware of the strength of anxiety from both the public and NHS staff, began consulting on targets for A&E waits. A 12-hour maximum was introduced quickly, followed by a promise of a four-hour waiting target.

The pressure on A&E was immense, and development of new ways of working was key to resolving the pressure. Amy Page took over as General Manager for Emergency Services to achieve the four-hour wait.

"It was a challenge to engage everyone, because it was seen as an A&E issue whereas actually it was a whole system issue. We had to change perceptions and practices."

Later in 2000, Ophthalmology moved to Pembury Hospital from Kent & Sussex, into both the old theatre and old radiotherapy buildings.

Trust Board 2002

Consultation Document

As part of the merger and changes in NHS there had been an understanding in many quarters, supported by government, that some services would need rationalising and centralising to support a critical mass of patients. This would give junior doctors better training and centralise expertise. But not everyone supported this idea, and as soon as a formal consultation was launched there were protests. The first consultation was for Women's and Children's Services, in September 2000.

A new hospital?
After years of false starts and campaigning, the Health Secretary Alan Milburn gave the go-ahead for a £160 million PFI scheme to replace Kent & Sussex and Pembury Hospitals in February 2001. The Courier screamed: 'Go-ahead for new hospital!'

The plans included a 450-bed hospital on one site, and managers expected it to become a reality by 2005. The plan did not focus on any one site, and many rumours of a hospital on various green field sites started. Plans were put on view for public comment in early 2002, as planning permission was sought to build on the Pembury site as the preferred option. The council gave planning permission in August 2002, quickly followed by approval from the health authority.

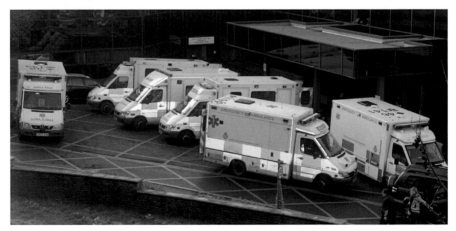

The crowded A&E entrance at Tunbridge Wells in 2005

The plan was put on hold when developer Kilmartin sought outline planning permission for a new hospital on the Knights Park area of Tunbridge Wells. The council would not grant permission, but did grant permission for a separate Pembury Hospital development by the trust.

Go-ahead for new hospital

The service bridge, demolished in 2005

In November 2002, a chimney blew down at the Kent & Sussex Hospital in a gale, damaging cars and narrowly missing Burslem House.

In April 2002, the Department of Health published its report 'Shifting the balance of power'. Primary Care Trusts were fully established and Health Authorities were merged into new Strategic Health Authorities. In Kent a new Kent & Medway Strategic Health Authority was established at Preston Hall.

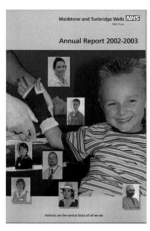
Annual Report

2003 was a difficult year for the Trust. At the start of the year Chief Executive Stephen Collinson, who had been appointed to the new Trust in April 2000, moved to take up a new position in London. An interim Chief Executive, Mark Davies, took over.

In February 2003, The Courier headlines screamed: 'Waiting list fiddle probe' relating to an investigation being carried out by Professor Robert Tinston, Professor of Healthcare at Manchester University. It found there were discrepancies between the real wait in some specialities and the figures reported. A number of staff were suspended and changes made to the way lists were audited.

Later, the trust scored zero stars in the national league tables. A new Chairman, James Lee, took over from Anne Chapman in the summer.

This was the year that junior doctors became subject to new legislation regarding working hours - leading to an increase in the number of junior doctors - and GPs were enabled to opt out of providing out-of-hours cover. This was an unsettling time, with much change in the NHS added to increasingly tougher targets. At the end of the year the Community Health Councils were abolished.

After much media speculation and rumour about the Trust and its direction and leadership, local MPs saw the Health Minister appealing for a new Chief Executive and Board to start to sort things out. The Courier headlines screamed: 'Health crisis in Whitehall's lap!'

At the end of November 2003, Rose Gibb arrived from Bromley Hospitals to take over as Chief Executive.

The planning inquiry, forced by a review into how and why planning permission was granted and the rival Kilmartin bid for Knights Park, threatened to overshadow progress to get the new hospital built. It was quickly followed by a judicial review, as Kilmartin claimed the process was flawed. Mr Justice Harrison considered it for nine days before backing Tunbridge Wells Borough Council. The findings from the inquiry were then sent to Deputy Prime Minister John Prescott for a final decision. In December 2003, Mr Prescott announced that the decision to give permission to build on the Pembury Site was sound.

Fire at the K&S May, 12th 2002

On the morning of 12th May 2002, a fire broke out on the top floor of the Kent & Sussex Hospital, in an area being renovated. Smoke soon billowed into the corridor and fire alarms echoed around the building. Within an hour over 12 fire engines were on the site, and widespread traffic delays resulted as roads were closed and film crews took up position. Clare Spence, on duty, described the response: *"Everyone knew what to do and there was no panic. It was incredibly scary to see the response and the smoke."*

As the situation developed further evacuation became necessary.
"We evacuated Ward 10 as fire fighting water was dripping through the ceiling, but the staff were magnificent and so efficient."

During summer 2004, the Kent & Sussex made the headlines as lifts failed in the Culverden Wing. Director of Nursing Bernard Place was interviewed as the lifts caused disruption. He highlighted the need for a new hospital whilst praising staff for their efforts.

In June 2004, BBC South East sent an undercover reporter into the Kent & Sussex Hospital to look at standards of cleaning. The resulting report was broadcast on BBC1. Over a million pounds was reinvested into cleaning standards, and a series of improvements started.

At the end of 2004 Chairman James Lee told the BBC:
"Almost everything had to change, and it's been an epic year for the trust."

The old and the new – the new hospital takes shape and overshadows the old ward blocks

New Government targets for A&E departments had been introduced. In 2003, the Trust was seeing 86% of patients through A&E in four hours, a year later 98% after the new four-hour treatment standard had been introduced.

The trust also had financial problems, with a £10 million debt to pay back at the same time as investing in services and maintaining poor building stock.

The PFI project started to gather pace, with a dedicated team launching the project. Jeanette Rooke, who was part of the team, said:

"It was a steep learning curve for all of us. The first real milestone was the bidders' day, when companies presented their ideas and concepts for the new hospital. That's when it dawned on us that it was really going to happen!"

The project team started to gather information from focus groups, and staff and patients looked at long-term commissioning intentions and health policy in order to establish what would need to go into the hospital.

As the team considered vacating the bottom end of the Pembury site and changing services across the Trust, a new Paediatric Unit opened at Pembury in January 2006. Elephant and Tiger Wards opened in the old 'F' Block, vacating Jacoby Ward and Rainbow Ward at the Kent & Sussex Hospital. At the same time a new Children's Emergency Assessment Unit opened at the Accident and Emergency Department at The Kent & Sussex Hospital.

Trust News highlights the new Children's Wards at Pembury

The huts at Pembury awaiting demolition – nature taking over.

Emergency Exercise 2004

Review of the PFI

The treasury review into PFI schemes put further obstacles in the way. PFI Director Graham Goddard recalled: *"The treasury review in 2006 was probably the time when the new hospital was in the greatest jeopardy. No trust could spend more than 15% of its income on a scheme. Our scheme exceeded that and had to be slimmed down to get past the Treasury. Several weeks of economic planning followed, including making open plan offices and taking out of the scheme services such as diabetes, which could be provided in a community setting. Eventually the scheme came in at 14.93% and crossed the hurdle."* Jeanette Rooke said: *"It was frustrating, but important that we got the affordability right."*

The Mental Health Unit was also removed by the Mental Health Trust, as a merger had taken place and a strategic estate review had concluded it was not needed.

In December 2006, it was announced that the Equion Consortium, comprising Interserve, John Laing and Laing O'Rourke, would build the new hospital.

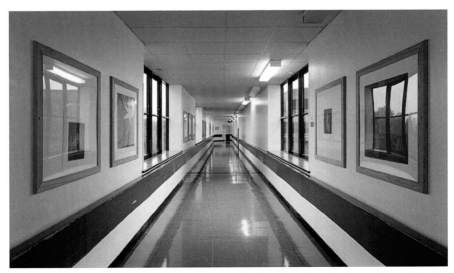

The Link Corridor at the Kent & Sussex Hospital

Credit crunch

In July 2006, MP Greg Clark asked the Prime Minister for a go-ahead for the new build once and for all. The Prime Minister promised an announcement within weeks, and in February 2007 the final go-ahead was announced. It was then announced that it would be the first NHS hospital to contain all single en suite rooms. Jeanette Rooke said: *"The DoH had committed us to at least 50% single rooms, but it became clear that the trust could be bold and innovative and make it the first UK NHS hospital with all single rooms."*

The whole scheme had another narrow escape in 2007, when the economy was hit by the credit crunch. Graham Goddard revealed that during final negotiations for a financial close the banks were already suffering from lack of funds, and only after government pressure was the scheme able to be signed off. He said: *"If it would have been just a few weeks later we would probably not have a new hospital."*

By late 2006, services were being moved off the bottom end of the Pembury site in preparation for the start of construction.

The site started to take on a windswept and overgrown appearance. The hospital had a number of planning restrictions on it, including the height of the buildings and the floor space allowed, which could not exceed what was there before. In addition, environmental factors had to be considered - including rehoming a large number of bats roosting in the buildings and various other animals including slow worms, dormice and other fauna and flora. The Trust had to construct a heated bat house in the grounds to house the bats, and provide for landscaping with natural native plants.

TRUST

NEWS

Maidstone and Tunbridge Wells NHS

July 2006

RETURN OF MATRON

NEW FACES • TOP FOOD AWARD FOR K&S CANTEEN • TRUST LAUNCHES INTO CYBER SPACE

The Government brought back matrons with a fanfare of publicity in July 2006, and Claire Spence and Christine Steele became Matrons of Kent & Sussex and Pembury respectively.

In 2006, a new Cardiac Catheter Centre opened at the Kent & Sussex Hospital.

A new Medical Director was appointed in January 2006, when Malcolm Stewart was appointed to a full-time role.

As part of the move, it was clear services would need to be reconfigured, and a public consultation was launched on the changes which would centralise trauma services at Pembury.

The Trust announced a consultation on moving services to one site, including a proposal to move all emergency surgery to Tunbridge Wells. A public consultation on surgical and orthopaedic services ran at the end of 2006, following various proposals going back to 2004, and sparked a fierce media campaign at Maidstone. The original consultation sparked a debate in Parliament in December 2004, when the Health Minister Melanie Johnson said anxiety was misplaced.

After a delay to rethink and consider timings with the new hospital, the consultation was relaunched. Kent County Council forced a decision to go to the Secretary of State, Alan Johnson. After the announcement of the consultation into trauma services across West Kent the Courier headlines screamed: 'New threat to town's hospital A&E Service!'

The Secretary of State referred the decision to an independent reconfiguration panel, which approved the decision in December 2007 after a three-month review.

In September 2006, the Strategic Health Authority announced an investigation into an outbreak of infection in the Trust, to be carried out by the Healthcare Commission. It followed a series of complaints and high-profile news stories about infections. In October the Health Care Commission published its report into the infection outbreaks at the Trust, and concluded that it was possible up to 90 patients could have died from or had an infection. National press and television focused on the report, which made headlines for several weeks.

At the end of 2006, Rose Gibb left the Trust, followed shortly afterwards by the Chairman. A new Chief Executive, Glenn Douglas, arrived to take the Trust forward.

In May 2007, the chapel was granted listed building status, to remain on the site as a testament and permanent link with the past. The Homeopathic Hospital, meanwhile, appeared in the headlines as the West Kent PCT decided not to commission homeopathy services, and the Maidstone & Tunbridge Wells NHS Trust withdrew services and staff from the building.

In February 2008, with demolition almost complete, the PFI was given the green light by the Strategic Health Authority. Local MP Greg Clark called it a 'momentous day' as Alan Johnson the Secretary of State gave the final green light in March 2008. Financial close of the project was another milestone, and as the team had floorplans agreed and a good deal of standardisation throughout the building, things could move fast.

Enabling Works start at Pembury with the creation of new roadways

Jeanette Rooke recalled:

"We had bulldozers on site within two days of close, and within weeks over 800 workers were on site starting the building process."

A special supplement was produced by the Courier to mark the occasion. Tunbridge Wells MP Greg Clark said:
"This will be the best hospital in the country, and it will put West Kent on the maps as a beacon of care in England."

In late 2007 and 2008, infection rates improved dramatically as more money and resources were invested into infection control, staffing and cleaning. Sally Magnusson hosted a BBC Panorama Programme from the hospital in April to consider what went wrong and how improvements were taking place, and in February 2008 Andrew Lansley, the Shadow Health Minister, visited the Trust.

Shortly afterwards, in January 2009, the Healthcare Commission announced that following inspections the Trust had 'improved substantially'.

Demolition of the Huts

Construction of the new buildings

The new hospital takes shape

The reality of a new hospital in Tunbridge Wells was made even more real when the topping-out ceremony took place on 12th June 2009, to mark the completion of the highest part of the building. Clare Spence, who had been involved in planning for the new hospital, said: *"The building almost appeared overnight, and we were conscious of how quickly we would move. Suddenly, from talking about services moving in years we were talking in weeks."*

The demolition of the old trust management building, revealing the original entrance carriageway

The name of the new hospital was always an issue that attracted much public comment. A plan to call it the Royal Tunbridge Wells Hospital was turned down as it was not in the Royal Borough, being in Pembury. Pembury Hospital, too, was felt inappropriate as it was associated with the old buildings. Eventually, the Tunbridge Wells Hospital at Pembury was decided upon.

The handover of Phase 1A was a major milestone. Jeanette Rooke recalled: *"We moved into the building on 20th November and literally worked on the floor with laptops to start with. The next day it snowed heavily and delayed all the deliveries to equip the hospital. The NHS spirit shined through and we just got on with it – it was so exciting. The building was so new."*

Construction of the new ICU and A&E in August 2008

The site in April 2008. The footings for the new building are visible

Staff celebrate the opening

On 25th January 2010, the first patients moved in to the new hospital from the old Pembury Hospital site. The day dawned damp and overcast but right on time the patients moved in. The operation to move patients was carefully planned, and despite clinical emergencies that occurred right up to the last minute, all patients were moved in safely and ahead of schedule. A survey carried out asking for views of those patients who were transferred revealed that 93% thought the transfer process was 'very good', while the remainder judged it 'good'. There was no negative feedback.

All new patients enjoyed not only single rooms but also flat screen digital televisions donated by the league of friends. The donation of over £270,000 was the biggest single donation ever made by the league in its history.

Demolition of the old buildings

Jeanette Rooke, who had co-ordinated the move and migration, said: *"I didn't really see the move as I was in the control centre, and I was really concerned. But I walked on to the Paediatric Ward and saw a little boy in his pyjamas heading to his single room to go to bed – for me that's what it was all about. This was it – patients were finally in and the hard work had paid off."*

In February 2010 the Kent County Council Health Overview and Scrutiny Committee referred to the Secretary of State for Health the decision to move maternity services from Maidstone. This led to further uncertainly over what services might move to Pembury. In December 2010 Health Secretary Andrew Lansley approved plans to move all inpatient women and children's services to Pembury from Maidstone. The move, which was opposed by some people in Maidstone, was welcomed by the Trust, which could now concentrate staffing and expertise on one site.

On May 19th 2011, the remaining part of the hospital was handed over to the Trust to begin commissioning and kitting-out the building. This started a huge commissioning operation. Jeanette Rooke said: *"In a way the experience of Phase 1A made it easier, and we had time to plan the moves."*

The next few months saw hundreds of staff trained at inductions, walk throughs, equipment commissioning and exercising, to make sure the building was ready. Over 200 Emergency Service personnel walked around to familiarise themselves with the building.

Meanwhile, at the Kent & Sussex, WRVS volunteers marked the end of their long association with the hospital. They ran a canteen and shop in Outpatients, along with other services, raising money for the hospital in the process and providing a cheerful service to staff and patients alike. In the new hospital a Costa Coffee and WH Smith would provide services and the Trust recognised the long service given by volunteers with a tea party to thank them.

There was a big rise in demand for services when the new building opened with mothers-to-be choosing the new hospital.

In April 2011, demolition started on the old buildings remaining on the Pembury Site. Cllr June Crowhurst, Chair of Pembury Parish Council, started the process with the old Woodlands House Nurses' Home.

On 5th August 2011, the media gathered at the front entrance of the Kent & Sussex Hospital to mark 50 days until the closure of the hospital. Staff released 50 balloons to mark the occasion.

As the move days got closer, detailed meetings with staff and partners such as Highways and Emergency Services took place to make sure that all eventualities were covered. Around the Kent & Sussex Hospital packing crates were starting to be filled, and staff were busy clearing out. Services such as Outpatients started to close and be moved over, with Inpatients services due to move in the following week.

The Jumbulance - ready to go

As 19th September dawned, there was an air of expectation around the site as patients began to get ready for the move. At the morning briefing meeting staff were briefed on the procedures and documentation to be used, including a major new trial of hospital evacuation paperwork. Meanwhile, staff had been working at Pembury ensuring wards were ready for receiving patients with all equipment checked and beds made.

By 9am a fleet of ambulances and a special jumbulance coach, adapted for patient movements, was ready to go, along with emergency services and extra staff. The Jumbulance was loaded, patients' property checked, and it was ready to go. The media took photos of this historic first journey and then, as Chief Executive Glenn Douglas climbed aboard to go with the first patients, there was a roar of police motorcycles. In an emotional atmosphere, patients waved as the traffic stopped, and the coach disappeared under police escort to the new hospital.

While there were a few moments to consider what was happening as the smell of diesel hung in the air, no time was lost packing and preparing the next wards. At Pembury, staff were waiting to escort the patients to their new wards, as a herald of police sirens brought the coach into the hospital. The Patient Transport Service and the Jumbulance moved over 100 patients in the first day.

On 20th September 2011, work continued, with more patients being transferred over to the new hospital. Director of Nursing Flo Panel-Coates said to the gathered media: *"Some of the staff came in at six o'clock this morning to get patients washed and dressed for the move. I'm so proud of them."*

The move went on all day, but then a strange quiet descended over the site as only A&E and ICU were left. Then at 2 am Will Bellamy, Duty Manager for the South East Coast Ambulance Service, made an announcement across the Ambulance Radio Network, broadcasting what everyone was waiting for: 'General Broadcast for all units in West Kent: please note that the Kent & Sussex Hospital is now closed, and the new Tunbridge Wells Hospital at Pembury is now fully open.' The press interviewed the staff on duty and took photos, and as the doors shut to the public for the last time the whole hospital took on a subdued feeling.

Staff continued to work, packing and clearing A&E while the doors were shut. Later that day, patients from Intensive Care were transferred to Pembury.

Once all patients were moved it fell to Chief Executive Glenn Douglas and Chief Nurse Flo Panel Coates to lock the front door in front of the gathered media and place the closed sign across the door. Inside, boarding up and clearing out continued a pace but it was not lost that 77 years of history had come to an end, and a new chapter in the history of healthcare in Tunbridge Wells was starting.

Director of Nursing, Flo Panel-Coates
and Chief Executive Glenn Douglas put the closed sign up

Over the next few months, the Kent & Sussex site was decommissioned, although Burslem House was retained for staff accommodation until an alternative could be found. By Christmas 2011 the site had started to get overgrown and neglected while a buyer was sought for the site. In April 2012 it was announced that Berkeley Homes had purchased the site for housing and demolition was planned for Summer 2013.

At the new Tunbridge Wells Hospital, staff and patients had settled in and were at last using the facilities destined to ensure that world-class healthcare could be continued into the 21st century. Jeanette Rooke said: *"We have a remarkable building. It feels calm and the flow plans really do work. We have regular showcase days, with visitors from all over the world. All of them comment on how fantastic the building is. It's a nice environment to work in and a nice environment to be treated in. It's the best in the country."*

The Kent & Sussex Hospital prepares to close

Patients arrive at the new hospital

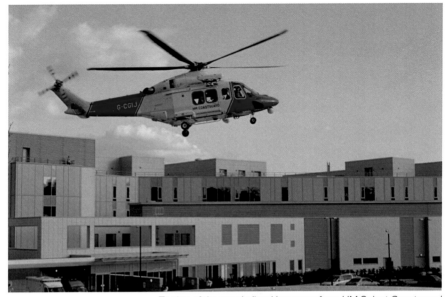

Testing of the new helipad by crews from HM Solent Coastguard

The site finished in 2012

The hospital was officially opened by HRH The Countess of Wessex on the 22nd March 2012. It marked the end of a huge project and a new chapter in the history of the hospitals in Tunbridge Wells started. New staff and visitors to the site hardly see a trace of the workhouse and victorian buildings that went before. A patient stood and looked and said

'its amazing, but how quickly we forget the past.'

Acknowledgements
In no particular order

We acknowledge the Courier
Newspaper Group for permission
to reproduce photographs held
by them.

Imperial War Museum

Centre for Kentish Studies –
Kent History Centre

Royal College of Physicians

Baroness Audrey Emerton

Tunbridge Wells Museum in
particular Ian Beavis

Janet Chitham

Kent County Council Registration Office
Tunbridge Wells in particular
Veronica Siddall and Stephen Bennett

Michael, Robin, Richard and
James Jacoby

Joan Page

Margaret Pilbeam

Kathy Chaney Salomons Museum

Francine Payne

Frank Stanford

Christopher Cassidy and the
Tunbridge Wells Project

Jane Bakowski

Annie Chellel

Neil Duncan

Jane Highland

Lucy Johnson

Bob Banks

Mike Everest

Jane Sutherland

Annette Sergeant

Bianca Hardy

Sue Stanbridge